KINGFISHER
COUNTRYSIDE
HANDBOOK

Michael Chinery

KINGFISHER BOOKS

Kingfisher Books, Grisewood and Dempsey Ltd,
Elsley House, 24–30 Great Titchfield Street,
London W1P 7AD

First published in 1990 by Kingfisher Books

BRITISH LIBRARY CATALOGUING IN PUBLICATION DATA
Chinery, Michael *1938–*
The countryside. – (Kingfisher handbook)
1. Great Britain. Countryside. 2. Europe. Countryside.
I. Title
941′.009′734

ISBN 0-86272-420-1

Edited by
Annabel Ramsbotham
Designed by Graham Davis
Phototypeset by Southern Positives and Negatives (SPAN),
Lingfield, Surrey
Printed in Italy

The publishers would like to thank the following artists for
contributing to the book:

Tessa Barwick (John Martin and Artists Ltd) pp. 30/31, 34–37,
56/57, 59–65, 147; Norma Burgin (John Martin and Artists
Ltd) p. 122; Stephen Crosby (John Martin and Artists Ltd) pp.
106/107, 149 (top), 150/151, 154/155, 157, 164–171, 174–177,
180/181; Steve Holden (John Martin and Artists Ltd) pp. 29,
72/73, 117; David Holmes (Garden Studio) cover, pp. 32/33, 48
(top left), 74, 85–87, 112–116, 118 (bottom), 132–137, 149
(bottom), 158–163, 184/185; Ron Jobson (Jillian Burgess
Artists) pp. 46/47; Eleanor Ludgate (Jillian Burgess Artists) pp.
12, 28, 50–53, 127, 128, 130/131, 139–143; Josephine Martin
(Garden Studio) pp. 8, 27, 40/41, 54/55, 71, 98–100, 120,
178/179, 182/183; David More (Linden Artists Ltd) pp. 21
(top), 22–26, 38 (top), 42–44, 45 (bottom), 48; Edward
Mortelmans (John Martin and Artists Ltd) pp. 21 (bottom), 38
(bottom), 49, 110/111, 118 (top), 173; Patricia Newell (John
Martin and Artists Ltd) pp. 45 (top), 77–83, 96/97, 103,
123–125, 144–146; Ralph Orme p. 9; Denys Ovenden pp.
66–69, 89, 90, 92/93, 105, 108/109; Glenn Steward (John
Martin and Artists Ltd) pp. 75, 84, 88; Anthea Toorchen (John
Martin and Artists Ltd) p. 119.

CONTENTS

EXPLORING THE COUNTRYSIDE

The countryside is made up of lots of different habitats, including mountains, rivers, woods, grasslands, and seashores. Each has its own collection of plants and animals and each has many secrets for you to uncover. This book will help you to put names to some of the plants and animals that you see and it will help you to discover how they live and what they do. It will also help you to understand how the different habitats came into existence and why the countryside in one part of the country looks so different from that in another part.

You don't need expensive equipment for studying the countryside. If you are interested in birds you will probably want some binoculars, and you will find them useful for watching other things as well. A pair of binoculars marked 8 × 30 is ideal for general use. They magnify things eight times.

Enjoy yourself in the countryside, but don't do anything to damage it. Keep to paths across farmland and fasten all gates behind you. Take all your litter home. If you follow these simple rules you will be helping other people to enjoy the countryside as well and you won't upset the farmers and other people that live there.

NOTE: A plant or animal marked with an asterisk ✳ does not occur naturally in Britain.

A LITTLE HISTORY

If you could travel back in time for half a million years you would find a very different countryside. You would also be very cold. Much of Europe was covered with ice at that time, for the world was in the middle of the Ice Age. Even 18,000 years ago most of Northern Europe was still under huge sheets of ice, known as glaciers. These moved slowly over the land, scraping and gouging the rocks like giant sheets of sandpaper. Large tracts of cold, bare land surrounded the ice sheets. Most of the plants and animals were confined to the warmer areas in the south of Europe.

But the earth was getting warmer and the glaciers were melting. Today they have nearly all gone, but we can find remnants of them in the far north and on some of the highest mountains. As the ice sheets melted, the land gradually turned green with plants spreading up from the south. Our present countryside was beginning to take shape.

In the far north, closest to the remaining ice, the land is still rather cold and bare. It is called the tundra. Similar areas exist on the cold and windswept mountain tops. To the south of the tundra, where the climate is a little warmer, a vast evergreen forest covers the land. It stretches right the way across northern Europe and consists mainly of cone-bearing trees, such as pines and spruces.

Areas shaded blue were covered with ice.
Areas shaded brown were land.

probably a glacial lake.

The map of Europe 18,000 years ago looks very different from the map of Europe today. Britain and Ireland were joined to the continent and the River Thames was a tributary of the River Rhine. But then the great ice sheets began to melt and pour their water back into the sea. The sea level rose about 90 metres during the next few thousand years and flooded large areas of the old land surface. Ireland became separated from the rest of Europe about 12,000 years ago, and Britain became separated about 7,000 years ago. The English Channel then formed a barrier to many of the plants and animals that were still spreading northwards. Britain and Ireland thus have far fewer kinds of plants and animals than neighbouring parts of the continent.

South of the coniferous forests, far from the remaining ice, we find the deciduous forests. These consist of oak, beech, ash, and other trees that drop their leaves in the autumn. In the far south, around the Mediterranean Sea, there is a third kind of forest. It is composed of tough-leaved evergreen oaks and pines.

About 10,000 years ago these kinds of forest covered almost the whole of Europe. But then people discovered how to grow crops and things began to change rapidly. The people started to cut down the forests to make way for the crops. They also cleared large areas for their sheep and cattle. The animals helped with this. Although they couldn't damage large trees, they nibbled most of the seedlings and prevented new trees from growing in many areas. Within a few thousand years nearly all the Mediterranean forests had disappeared and most of the deciduous forests had been converted to the fields and meadows that make up most of today's countryside.

The tundra is very cold. For much of the year it is covered with snow and the ground is frozen solid. But for a few weeks in the summer it warms up and flowers can spring up to colour the ground. In some places the ground may be completely covered with flowers. Large areas of Europe looked like this during the Ice Age.

When the ice-age glaciers flowed down from the mountains they gouged out deep U-shaped valleys like this one on the Alps. If you find a U-shaped valley you can be sure that it once contained a glacier.

This glacier in Iceland is like a gigantic river of ice. Formed by thousands of years of heavy snow, it flows slowly down the hillside and melts when it reaches the coast.

Glaciers grind up the rocks as they move along and they carry the broken material away with them. When they finally melt, the debris is left in a thick layer all over the ground. One of the commonest forms of glacial debris is boulder clay, which is a thick clay containing stones and boulders of all sizes. Boulder clay is to be found all over the northern half of Europe.

THE ROCKS AROUND YOU

The earth is made up of lots of different kinds of rocks. Most of them are very hard, like granite and limestone, but there are also some very soft rocks, like clay. These soft rocks are easily worn away by rain and rivers to form broad valleys and lowlands. Hard rocks are not easily worn away and they stand out to form the hills and uplands. This means that the shape of the countryside or landscape depends on the rocks underneath it. The type of vegetation also depends on the underlying rocks, because different kinds of rocks give rise to different kinds of soil. Some plants like sandy soils, while others like chalky soils or even heavy clay soils.

LOOKING FOR ROCKS

Try to find out what kinds of rocks make up the countryside around your home. Look for them in quarries and where new roads cut through the hills. The rocks may also be exposed on building sites and even in minor roadworks. Other good places to see rocks include seaside and river cliffs and mountain slopes.

The Whin Sill is a band of hard volcanic rock stretching across Northern England. In places it stands above the softer rocks like a black cliff. Parts of Hadrian's Wall, built by the Romans as a defence against the Picts, were built on the top of this cliff.

Even hard rocks do not last for ever. Shattered by frost and battered by wind and rain, these rocks have taken on weird shapes as they are gradually worn away. Even high mountains eventually crumble away, but new rocks are always being formed from the debris.

HOW THE ROCKS WERE FORMED

Most of the rocks around us were formed under the sea. We know this because many of them contain the remains of sea creatures. The rocks were formed from the sediments that accumulated on the sea bed, so they are called *sedimentary rocks*. The sediments included the sand and mud brought down by the rivers, as well as the material bashed from the cliffs by the waves. These sediments were gradually compressed to form the rocks. Powerful movements inside the earth eventually lifted the new rocks out of the sea. Rocks are still being formed by this process today.

THE COMMONEST ROCKS

► Sandstone rocks were formed where layers of sand accumulated on the sea bed. The grains are tightly packed and stuck together, but otherwise the rocks look just like the sand that you find on the beach. Some sandstones crumble easily, but others are very hard.

Clay rocks were usually formed far out at sea, where the very finest mud settled on the sea-bed.

▼ Limestone rocks were usually formed in shallow seas where there was little sand or mud. Lime was deposited from the warm water and it formed thick layers of rock. The clear water teemed with animals and some limestones consist almost entirely of their shells cemented together with the lime. Chalk is a limestone made up of the shells of microscopic creatures called *forams*. It is softer than most other limestones.

The mountain limestone exposed at Malham Cove in Yorkshire is clearly divided into layers, with the oldest layers at the bottom. Most sedimentary rocks are layered like this because they were formed from layers of sediment falling on to the sea-bed. But the layers are not always horizontal: many rocks buckled when they were lifted by earth movements and their layers now slope in all directions.

Churches and country cottages are often built with local stone or rock and they can tell you quite a lot about the local geology. This pack horse bridge in Suffolk, England is built largely with flints, the hard stones that are commonly found in the chalk. Flint is a very useful material and it was used for axes and many other tools by people in the Stone Age.

Not all rocks are formed on the sea-bed. Some come from deep in the earth, where the temperature is high enough to melt them. They are called *igneous rocks*, which means 'rocks of fire'. From time to time weak parts of the earth's crust split open and allow the red hot molten rocks to gush out. These fiery openings are called volcanoes. The one in the picture is in Iceland, where there are several volcanoes that can erupt and pump out fresh rock at any time. The molten rock

is called *lava*. It can flow for many miles before cooling down and turning into hard rock.

As they cooled down, many ancient lava flows split into huge six-sided columns like these at the Giant's Causeway in Ireland. You can see a similar process taking place when muddy ground dries up and the mud cracks into six-sided plates.

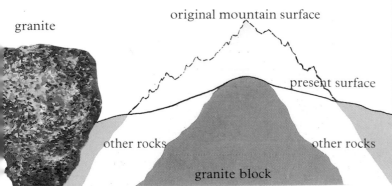

granite

original mountain surface

present surface

other rocks

other rocks

granite block

Granite is a very common igneous rock full of large crystals. It is usually associated with mountains. When the mountains are formed a lot of molten rock is pushed up under them, but it does not reach the surface. Deep under the other rocks, it cools very slowly and this allows the crystals to reach their large size. The granite does not become visible until the overlying rocks are worn away, so the granite that we see around us today is a rather ancient rock. Most of the Scottish mountains are made of granite. You can see lots of granite in Cornwall and Brittany and also in Germany's Black Forest.

NATURAL HOT WATER

This fountain is one of Iceland's famous *geysers* – hot springs that shoot boiling water into the air every few minutes. Geysers are quite common in volcanic areas because hot rocks are never far from the surface. Water trickling through the rocks collects in cavities in hot areas and heats up rapidly. As soon as it starts to boil the steam shoots the water into the air.

Although Iceland is a cold country, with lots of glaciers, there is a lot of hot water under the ground – enough to heat all the houses in the capital, Reykjavik. The Icelandic people even grow bananas in greenhouses heated with this natural hot water.

cross-section of the ground beneath a geyser.

Fossils are the shells and other remains of animals and plants that have been preserved in the rocks. The creatures were living in or around the sea when the rocks were being formed, and when they died their bodies became buried in the sand and mud that later turned to rock. People used to think that the Devil had planted the fossils in the rocks.

WHERE TO FIND FOSSILS

You can find fossils in lots of different rocks, but limestones are the best. The fossils are often harder than the surrounding rock and they stick out as the rock is worn away. Beaches below the cliffs are sometimes good places to look for fossils. Only the sedimentary rocks, which were formed from layers of sediment, contain fossils. You will not find any in granite or other igneous rocks.

ammonite

Devil's toe nail

sea urchin

sea lily

trilobite

fossil plant

THE CONIFEROUS FOREST

A huge forest of cone-bearing trees stretches right across Northern Europe. You could walk for weeks and still not get to the edge of this great evergreen forest. The commonest trees are the Norway spruce and the Scots pine. Only small patches of natural pine forest now remain in Britain. You must go to Scandinavia to see a really big coniferous forest. There are also forests of cone-bearing trees on the slopes of the Alps and other high mountains.

The cone is where the seeds are made. The cones are small and red at first, but they swell and turn green as the seeds grow inside them. When the seeds are ripe the cones become brown and woody.

CONIFER PLANTATIONS

Most of the timber used for building houses comes from cone-bearing trees. These are often grown in large plantations. Lots of different kinds of conifers are grown in plantations. They have many uses. The resin being collected from this pine will be used for making paints and varnishes.

SCOTS PINE

pollen cones

young cones

unripe cones

ripe cone scattering seeds

Attractive brick-red bark on the upper part of the trunk tells you that you are looking at a Scots pine. This is the only pine native to the British Isles, but it grows in most other parts of Europe as well.

Like nearly all European pines, the Scots pine carries its tough, needle-like leaves in pairs on tiny stalks.

Look for the young cones in the spring. They are small and red and they appear at the tips of the shoots. Further back you will see clusters of small yellow cones. Shake them and watch the clouds of pollen drift away. The red cones cannot swell up and make their seeds until they have been dusted with some of this pollen.

The Norway spruce is the Christmas tree. Millions of young spruces are grown every year just for us to decorate at Christmas.

The smaller branches all droop, so snow slides off them easily and the tree doesn't mind growing in very cold areas. It is the commonest tree in the northern forests. It is not a native of Britain, but it is grown in lots of plantations to provide timber.

Spruce needles are flat and they grow singly on short wooden stalks. When the needles eventually fall the stalks remain on the twigs like little stumps. This separates the spruces from all other conifers.

Norway spruce cones are about 12cm long. They hang from the branches and do not fall to pieces when their seeds are ripe.

The larch is a graceful tree, with leafy twigs hanging from the branches like little green chains. It is an unusual conifer because it drops all its leaves for the winter. The leaves grow in little tufts, which sprout from stumpy side-shoots every spring. They are bright green at first, but get darker in the summer and then turn golden yellow in the autumn.

Because the larch drops its leaves for the winter, there is plenty of light underneath it in the spring. Lots of spring flowers can grow there. The natural home of the larch is in the Alps and other mountains.

Larch cones start life looking like small pink roses. They become brown and woody as their seeds ripen, and they often stay on the trees for several years after scattering the seeds.

The silver fir is a tree of the mountains. It forms thick forests in the Alps and the Pyrenees. You can usually recognise it by its rather pale bark. It is the largest of the European conifers, often growing over 50m high. It keeps its conical shape for much of its life.

The needles have silvery bands underneath, giving the tree its name. They are arranged on two sides of the twig, a bit like the teeth of a two-sided comb. Each one is attached by a little sucker and it leaves a neat round scar when it falls.

The cones are green to start with and they always stand upright on the branches. They fall to pieces when they are ripe.

young female catkin

male catkin

The BIRCH was the first tree to appear when the ice-age glaciers melted. It is very hardy. It grows quickly, but it never gets very big and it does not live long. Other trees gradually crowd it out. The birch grows happily in the far north and is common in forest clearings. You can usually recognise mature birch trees by the white bark.

The tiny flowers form catkins. Male catkins appear in the autumn, but do not open and scatter pollen until the spring. Female catkins appear amongst the leaves. They swell as the seeds grow inside them, and they hang down when they are ripe.

The leaves become golden yellow before they fall in the autumn.

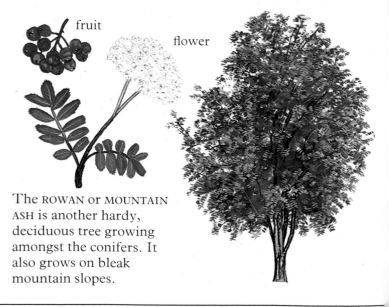

fruit

flower

The ROWAN or MOUNTAIN ASH is another hardy, deciduous tree growing amongst the conifers. It also grows on bleak mountain slopes.

The BILBERRY is one of the commonest plants growing under the pines and spruces of the northern forests. It also grows on moorland (see p. 127). Its greenish pink flowers look like little lanterns in the spring. In late summer they produce purplish black berries.

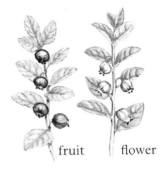

fruit   flower

Lots of coniferous woods are full of BRACKEN. This is the world's commonest fern. It grows best on sandy soil, but it needs shelter from the wind in cold areas. Unlike most ferns, the bracken has creeping underground stems. These can grow more than a metre in a year, so the fern spreads rapidly through the woods. The young leaves are tightly curled for protection as they push up through the soil in the spring. Fully grown leaves may be over four metres high. They become golden brown as they die down in the autumn.

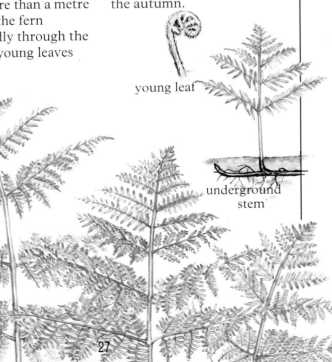

young leaf

underground stem

You won't find many flowers in the coniferous forests. Most plants need light to make their food and there is just not enough light for them under the evergreen trees. Low temperatures are also a problem. The old pine and spruce needles decay very slowly in the cold, and not many plants can grow in the thick layer of needles that builds up.

◀ The VIOLET BIRD'S-NEST ORCHID has no green parts at all. Its roots combine with tiny fungi in the soil, and together they break down the dead needles to release food. Because the plant does not make food in the normal way, it can survive in the dark forest. It grows in the mountain forests of southern and central Europe.

▶ The TWINFLOWER gets its name because its flowers always grow in pairs. It can make some food in its green leaves but, like the violet bird's-nest orchid, it gets most of its food from the dead leaves with the help of fungi.

The FLY AGARIC sometimes grows under spruce trees, but is most common under birch and pine. It is very poisonous.

◀ Toadstools can feed on wood as well as on leaves. This one, called PLUMS-AND-CUSTARD, grows on pine stumps. It gets its name from its red and yellow colour.

Some toadstools are very fussy about their food. This one grows only on dead cones. It has no common name.

You must never eat fungi unless you are **absolutely sure that they are safe**. Many toadstools are poisonous.

◀ This weird growth is a CAULIFLOWER FUNGUS. It grows on and around pine stumps and may be as big as a football.

Squirrels love to eat the seeds of pine and spruce cones. Look for the remains of cones to discover where the animals feed. They often use tree stumps as tables. All that remains of a cone is the central stalk, with a little tuft of scales at the tip. Red squirrels are found only in pine woods in Britain, but elsewhere in Europe they live in all kinds of woods. The grey squirrel (see p. 48) lives only in Britain. It is common in parks and gardens as well as in woods. Both kinds of squirrels strip cones to get at the seeds.

On the track of the red squirrel

Look for the squirrel's footprints in snow and muddy paths.

BE A WILDLIFE DETECTIVE

Lots of different animals feed on pine and spruce seeds. They all have their own ways of opening the cones. Mice gnaw the cones like squirrels, but they are usually a bit neater. The mice are also shy, and they eat their meals in sheltered places. Woodpeckers twist and tear the scales, leaving the cones looking very ragged. They often wedge the cones into bark crevices before attacking them. The crossbill uses its strange beak to force the cone scales apart. It often splits the scales in half in the process.

crossbill

crossbill

woodpecker

squirrel   mouse

✳ black woodpecker

31

✱

The ELK is the largest of all the deer. It is two metres or more high at the shoulders and the male's antlers span about two metres. Females don't have antlers. The elk lives in the forests of Scandinavia and eats the leaves, twigs, and bark of all kinds of trees. It is especially fond of willows. It is particularly common around lakes and rivers, and in the summer it wades in to eat water lilies and other plants.

On the track of the elk

The elk's footprint is about 15cm long – much longer than anything else of its kind.

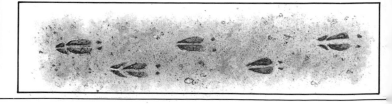

The mammals pictured here are all shy and come out to hunt mainly at night. You will have to go to really wild places to find them. Few people are ever lucky enough to track them down.

The WILD CAT lives in Scotland and also in the Alps and some of the forests of southern Europe. It looks like an overgrown tabby cat, but it has a much bushier tail with broad black rings.

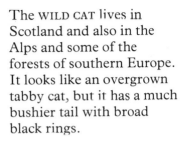

The PINE MARTEN is a great climber and acrobat. It chases birds and squirrels at high speed through the tree tops. It also catches mice and voles on the ground.

The LYNX is a large, long-legged cat with a short tail. It is a rare animal, living in the northern forests and on some of the mountains in southern Europe.

*

male

female

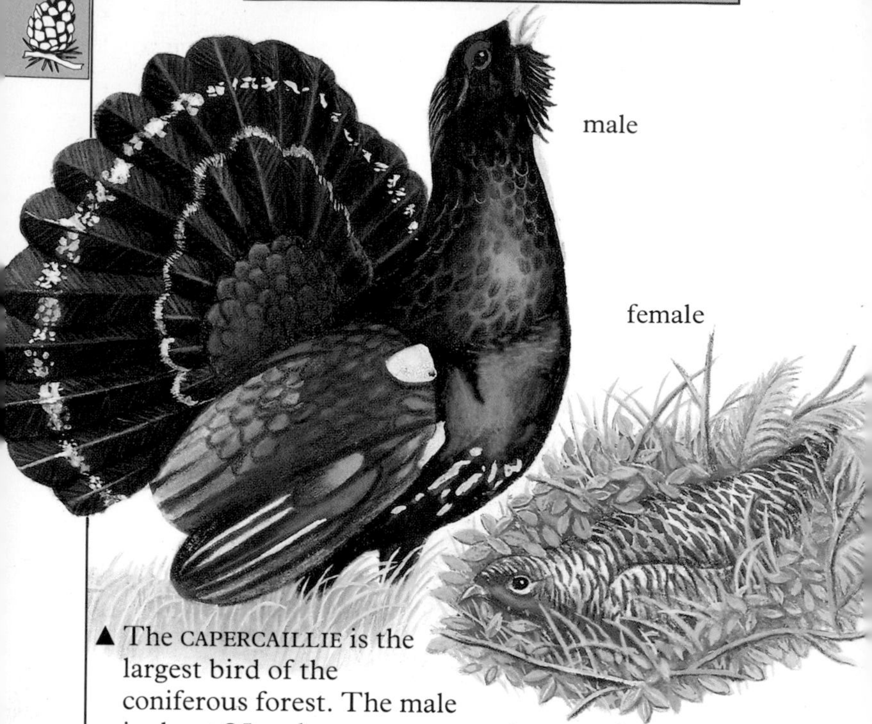

▲ The CAPERCAILLIE is the largest bird of the coniferous forest. The male is about 85cm long, although his mate is only about 60cm long. The birds feed mainly on the young leaves and buds of the conifers, but they come down to the ground in the summer to eat bilberries and insects. The males join forces in the spring to attract females with song and dance displays.

◄ The GOLDCREST is the smallest bird of the northern forest. It is nine centimetres long. It can be found in woods all over Europe.

male

▼ The FIRECREST is the same size as the goldcrest. It lives in all kinds of woodlands but does not reach the northern forests.

female

▶ The BRAMBLING breeds in the far north. It is one of the commonest birds in the birch woods on the northern edge of the coniferous forest. It moves south into the deciduous woodlands for the winter and often joins flocks of chaffinches to feed on beechnuts.

summer

male

female

◀ The CRESTED TIT is easily recognised by the spiky black and white feathers which form a crest on its head. It can be found in coniferous woods in most parts of Europe.

▶ The WAXWING gets its name from the waxy red blobs on its wing feathers. It nests among the conifers and birches of the far north, but moves south for the winter. It occasionally visits parks and gardens to feed on berries.

Owls are designed for nightwork. Their big eyes are a hundred times better than ours at spotting things in the dark. The birds also have amazing hearing and can hear the slightest rustle in the grass from high in the air. Their wing feathers have fluffy edges and make no noise as they swoop down to snatch their prey.

▼ The EAGLE OWL is Europe's largest owl. It is 70cm long and weighs up to three kilograms. It feeds mainly on large birds.

✳

► What look like ears on the LONG-EARED OWL are just tufts of feathers. The birds' real ears are hidden under the feathers at the sides of the head.

▲ The OSPREY feeds almost
▶ entirely on fish. It circles
over lakes and rivers and
plunges down when it spots
a fish. It enters the water
feet-first with a great
splash, but it doesn't hurt
itself because its legs and
feet are strongly built.
Sharp spines under the toes
help the bird to hold the
slippery fishes securely.

*

◀ Most owls hunt by night,
but the GREAT GREY OWL
hunts by day. It doesn't
need such big eyes as the
eagle owl. These two owls
look much the same size,
but the great grey owl is
nearly all feathers. It
weighs only half as much as
the eagle owl.

37

THE DECIDUOUS FOREST

The deciduous forests are made up mainly of trees that drop their leaves in the autumn. Some forests have lots of different kinds of trees, but one kind is usually more common than the rest. This is called the dominant tree.

Most deciduous forests have four distinct layers. The top-most layer is the canopy. formed by the leaves and branches of the tallest trees. Below this there is usually a layer of shrubs or small trees. Below the shrubs comes the herb layer, made up of flowers and ferns. The fourth layer is the ground layer, made up of mosses and toadstools. Each layer is full of interesting animal life, so there is plenty for you to see in the forest.

BARK RUBBINGS

You can often recognize trees just by looking at their bark. Many of them have interesting patterns. You can make copies of these bark patterns by holding a big sheet of paper firmly against the trunk and rubbing it with a thick wax crayon. It is easier if you get someone to hold the paper while you rub it. Bark rubbings can make interesting 'posters' for your walls.

Because the deciduous trees drop their leaves in the autumn, the forests look very different at different times of the year. Don't ignore the forest in winter. Deer are often easier to see then, and if it snows you can spot all kinds of animal tracks.

In the **spring**, when the tree leaves are just opening, lots of light reaches the forest floor. Lots of small plants are able to flower then.

Not much light reaches the forest floor in the **summer** and you won't find many flowers. Many of the plant leaves get bigger to trap as much light as possible.

Autumn is a colourful season. The leaves turn from green to red and gold as they prepare to fall. Colourful toadstools appear on the forest floor.

The trees are resting in **winter**, and this is a good time to look at their buds. Each bud is a parcel of tiny leaves, well wrapped up against the cold winds.

It is easy to recognize a beech tree: look for the smooth grey bark. In the winter you can also identify the tree by its long, pointed buds.

fruit

female

winter buds

Like many forest trees, the beech has two kinds of flowers. The male, pollen-producing flowers form fluffy catkins that look like tiny feather dusters. The female flowers are very tiny, but in the autumn they produce triangular brown nuts in spiky cases. The nuts are good to eat, but fiddly to open.

male

Beech trees like well-drained soil and some of the best beech woods grow on the chalk hills. Very few plants can grow under the beech trees because it is too dry and too shady.

THE ASH

The ash is one of the last trees to open its leaves in the spring. Each leaf is divided into several separate leaflets, and a large leaf may be 30cm long.

During the winter you can easily recognise the ash tree by its sooty black buds. The ash grows best on damp, rich soils, especially in limestone areas. It does not cast much shade and lots of plants can grow underneath it.

The flowers appear just before the leaves, forming dense purplish clusters on the twigs. They produce bunches of fruits called keys, which eventually get blown away by the wind. Try throwing some in the air on a windy day to see how far they travel before falling to the ground.

buds

flowers

fruit

leaf

male catkins

Oak trees can generally be recognized by their deeply-lobed leaves, and by their acorns sitting in little cups.

There are lots of different kinds of oaks, the commonest one being the PEDUNCULATE OAK. This name means *stalked,* and if you look at the acorns you will see that each is carried at the end of a slender stalk. The pedunculate oak likes deep, rich soils and grows particularly well in the lowlands. In dense forests it grows tall and straight, but when it has room, it spreads its branches freely and is then super for climbing.

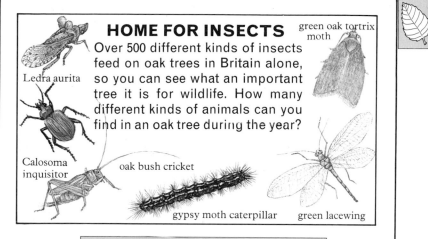

HOME FOR INSECTS

Over 500 different kinds of insects feed on oak trees in Britain alone, so you can see what an important tree it is for wildlife. How many different kinds of animals can you find in an oak tree during the year?

Ledra aurita

green oak tortrix moth

Calosoma inquisitor

oak bush cricket

gypsy moth caterpillar

green lacewing

SOME OTHER OAKS

◀ The SESSILE OAK is very like the pedunculate oak, except that its acorns sit on the twigs with little or no stalk. This tree prefers the poorer soils and is more commonly found in the uplands.

▶ The TURKEY OAK has more deeply-cut leaves than the other European oaks and its acorn cups are frilly. Its buds are also rather whiskery. The tree is a native of southern Europe.

*

◀ DOWNY OAK is a fairly small oak growing in southern and central Europe. Its leaves are not deeply lobed and they are velvety underneath when they are young. The twigs and buds are also covered with soft grey hairs.

A tree trunk gets thicker every year, by adding a ring of new wood just under the bark. You can see these rings of wood, called *annual rings*, quite easily when a tree is cut down. By counting them you can find out the age of the tree – one ring for every year.

But there is an easier way to discover the age of a tree, and you don't have to cut the tree down. Tree expert Alan Mitchell discovered that most trees, when growing by themselves with plenty of room to spread their branches, add about 2.5cm to the girth or circumference of the trunk each year.

So by measuring the girth of a tree trunk at about 1.5m above the ground, you can get a pretty good idea of the age of the tree. A tree 250cm around the trunk will be about 100 years old, but remember that trees growing close together in the woods grow rather more slowly.

HOW TALL IS THAT TREE?

All you need to measure the height of a tree is a straight stick exactly the same length as the distance from your eye to your outstretched hand. Hold the stick upright, as shown in the picture, and walk backwards or forwards until the stick appears to be the same size as the tree. The distance from you to the base of the tree will then be the same as the height of the tree. Measure the distance with a measuring tape.

How tall is the tallest tree you can find? What kind of tree is it?

Remember that the method works only if your stick is the right length and if you hold it straight out in front of you. You can test the accuracy of the method by trying it on a church tower or other tall building with a known height.

Most people like to eat hazel nuts. Hundreds of years ago these tasty nuts were a very important food for our ancestors. Even 100 years ago people used to arrange 'nutting parties' to gather the ripe nuts in the autumn. Such feasts are not possible now in Britain, thanks to the grey squirrel. This animal, which was introduced from North America about 100 years ago, loves hazel nuts. It strips most of them from the trees even before they are ripe and it leaves very few for us to gather.

The hazel is common in our hedgerows and woodlands, where it has lived under the oaks and ashes for thousands of years. Our ancestors had lots of uses for its supple branches. We still use hazel today for making hurdle fences and for garden bean poles.

▼ When the catkins are open, search the twigs for buds with tiny red 'feathers' on them. These are the nut-producing flowers. The nuts start to grow when pollen falls on the feathery bits.

▲ Each nut is held in a leafy cup. The bit that we eat is the seed inside the nut.

◄ The hazel's pollen-producing flowers form long yellow catkins, often called lambs' tails. They are some of the first flowers to open in the spring.

COPPICED WOODLAND

The trees in this patch of woodland have recently been cut down, but new shoots are already sprouting strongly from the stumps. In a few years there will be a dense wood again. Most woods used to be treated like this to provide regular supplies of timber for fences, firewood, and many other things. A different area was cut each year. After about 15 years the trees in the first area were ready for another cut and the cycle began again. But not all the trees were cut down. Some were left to grow into mature trees to provide large timber for building. This system is called *coppicing*. It is still used in some woodlands today, especially on nature reserves. Flowers grow particularly well in the first few years after coppicing, when lots of light reaches the ground.

These trees were cut down to about two metres above the ground and new branches sprouted. This system is called *pollarding* and it is used instead of coppicing in areas where there are lots of deer. Coppicing is no good in such areas because the deer eat the tender young shoots. But they can not reach the young shoots on the pollarded trees.

You can find hundreds of different kinds of wild flowers in the deciduous woodlands. Most of them appear in the spring, before the trees spread their leaves and cast too much shade on the ground. The flowers nearly all grow best in open woodland, especially in areas that are coppiced regularly (see p. 49). Some flowers like damp soils and some like well-drained soils. If you find that the plants change dramatically as you walk through a wood, you can be sure that you are walking over different kinds of soil.

◀ WOOD SORREL goes to sleep at night. Its flowers close up and nod their heads, and its leaves fold up. The plant is common in the drier parts of woods. It often grows on rocks and tree trunks.

▶ You will always know when you are near a patch of RAMSONS, because the plant smells strongly of garlic. It carpets large areas of damp woodland, even in quite shady areas.

◀ HERB PARIS has nothing to do with France. Its name comes from a Latin word meaning *equal*, and it refers to the four equal leaves at the top of the stem. Each star-like green flower produces a large black berry. The plant likes damp woods, and if you find it you can be sure that you are in a really old wood.

▲ BLUEBELLS form thick
▶ carpets on sandy soils.
They will grow in beech-
woods if the trees are not
too close together. The
leaves die down after
flowering and the plant
spends much of the year
resting as a bulb under the
ground.

◀ The BIRD'S-NEST ORCHID
gets its name because its
roots are clustered together
rather like a bird's nest. It
is one of the few plants that
can grow in dense
beechwoods. It does not
need sunlight because it has
no leaves and makes no
food for itself. It gets all its
food from the decaying
beech leaves.

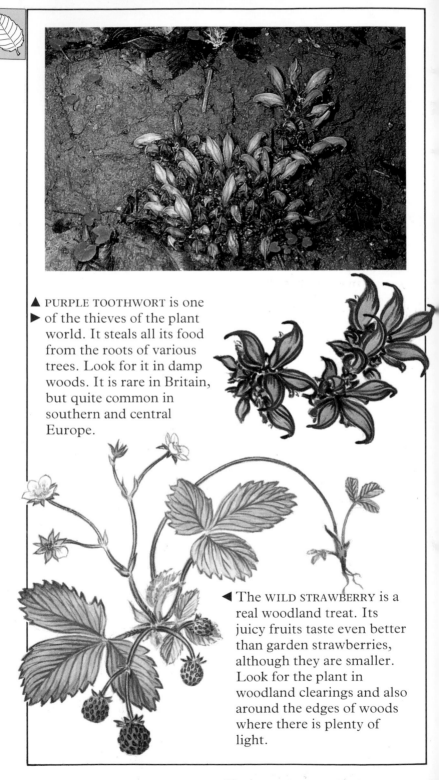

▲ PURPLE TOOTHWORT is one
► of the thieves of the plant
world. It steals all its food
from the roots of various
trees. Look for it in damp
woods. It is rare in Britain,
but quite common in
southern and central
Europe.

◄ The WILD STRAWBERRY is a
real woodland treat. Its
juicy fruits taste even better
than garden strawberries,
although they are smaller.
Look for the plant in
woodland clearings and also
around the edges of woods
where there is plenty of
light.

◀ STINKING HELLEBORE is a rather smelly plant of dry woodlands, especially in limestone areas. Its flowers open as early as January in some places. They have no petals. What look like petals are actually the sepals.

▼ HERB ROBERT is very common on the edges of woodland paths, especially in stony places. It has a strong smell, rather like that of a fox. The leaves often turn bright red in summer. No-one knows how the plant got its name.

▶ ROSEBAY WILLOWHERB is often called fireweed, because it is one of the first plants to spring up on burnt ground. Look for it on roadsides and waste land as well as in woodland clearings.

Ferns don't have flowers or seeds. They simply scatter clouds of brown dust in dry weather. The dust particles are called *spores* and new ferns can grow from them.

If you look at the undersides of the leaves you will see the brown patches where the spores are formed. It's very easy to grow your own ferns by shaking a few spores on to a dish of damp soil. Keep it moist and the spores will soon start to grow. New ferns cannot develop without moisture, and this is why most ferns grow in damp, shady places. Most of them will grow well indoors, as long as you water them regularly.

▼ HARD FERN is also called ladder fern because of the special ladder-like leaves on which its spores develop.

▲ Fern leaves are always tightly curled when young.

▼ HART'S-TONGUE FERN is one of the few ferns with undivided leaves.

Many ferns, like this POLYPODY FERN, grow on walls and tree trunks in damp climates. Their roots soak up rainwater and moisture from the air.

PLANTED BY BIRDS

Mistletoe grows on the branches of trees instead of on the ground. It uses all sorts of trees, but oak, poplar, and apple are its favourites. Look for this strange plant on the edges of woods as well as on roadside and orchard trees. The best time to look is in the winter, when the trees have lost their leaves. The evergreen mistletoe then shows up clearly as large green clusters. The mistletoe can make its own food, but it has to steal water and minerals from the branches on which it grows. Birds like the white berries, but the seeds stick to their beaks. They get rid of the seeds by wiping their beaks on the branches. The seeds are then in just the right place to grow into new mistletoe plants.

THE TIMID DEER

Deer are shy animals and you must be very quiet if you want to watch them in the forest. Their footprints, called *slots*, will give you some idea where to look for the animals. But they are quite difficult to spot because they are well camouflaged. All of them are greyer in the winter than they are in the summer coats that you can see here. Only the males have antlers. They use them to wrestle with each other in the breeding season. The antlers fall off after the breeding season, but new ones soon start to grow. You won't often find the old ones because the deer usually eat them.

red

The red deer is our largest deer apart from the elk (see p. 32).

Fallow deer have broad antlers and a black tail. The spots disappear in the winter. The roe deer is our smallest native deer.

fallow

roe

BE A WILDLIFE DETECTIVE

stripped sapling

badger hair

Many animals leave signs or clues that show you where they have been walking or feeding. If you can find the clues you will know where to watch for the animals, because they often use the same paths and feeding places each day.

Tufts of greyish hair on fences and hedges show where badgers trundle through.

Deer strip the bark from sapling trees, starting at the bottom and leaving ragged strips further up.

deer footprints

Lots of different animals eat hazel nuts and each one has its own way of opening them. Squirrels split them neatly in half. Woodmice chew holes in them and leave toothmarks all round the edge of the hole. Voles also chew holes in the shells, but there are no tooth-marks around the edge. Wood-peckers wedge the nuts in bark crevices and hammer them open with their beaks. There are usually beak marks around the jagged hole. Empty shells are pulled out and left on the ground so that the crevice can be used again.

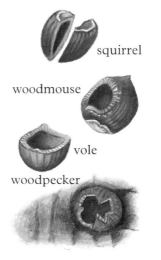

squirrel

woodmouse

vole

woodpecker

fox   dog

THE FOX

The fox is a beautiful animal, but it doesn't smell very nice. It leaves its smell wherever it goes, so it's not difficult to tell if there's a fox about. The best way to find out what it smells like is to visit a fox in a zoo. You won't forget the smell in a hurry! Foxes are active mainly at night, and the best time to see them is at dusk. If you get up early you might also see them going home at daybreak. They live in dens called *earths*. They often take over old rabbit holes or even share a badger's home. Foxes eat all kinds of animals, from worms and beetles to rabbits and birds. Look for footprints on woodland paths. They are quite like dog prints, but the outer toes of a fox are further back. The fox's bushy tail is called a *brush*.

BROCK THE BADGER

The badger doesn't usually come out until after dark. The best way to see it is to find its home, called a *set*, and then go back just before nightfall. Sit quietly and you'll probably see this lovely animal trundle out to look for food. But it won't come out if it can smell you, so make sure that any wind is blowing from the set to you and not the other way round. Lots of badgers often live in one set and there may be several entrance holes. There is usually a lot of bare ground around the set, with big heaps of excavated soil. Badgers eat all sorts of things, from bluebell bulbs to baby rabbits, but their favourite food is earthworms. Brock is an old country name for the badger.

▶ The NIGHTINGALE is famous for its beautiful song. It sings by day as well as by night, but you can hear the song better at night because most of the other birds are quiet. The bird is a summer visitor to Europe, but few people ever see it because it is shy and keeps to the dense shrub layer in the woods.

◀ If you've ever tried cracking a cherry stone you'll know just how strong the HAWFINCH is. It has no trouble in cracking the stones in its fat beak. It usually splits them cleanly in half. Look for the empty shells under cherry trees in gardens and orchards as well as in the woods.

▶ The BULLFINCH is a beautiful bird, but it is also a bit of a pest. It feeds mainly on buds in the spring and does a lot of damage in orchards. You will nearly always see the birds in pairs.

The CHIFFCHAFF got its name because its song sounds just like *chiff-chaff*, repeated again and again. It is a common summer visitor to most parts of Europe, but it is not easy to spot because it usually stays high in the trees.

▲ The SPOTTED FLYCATCHER is often mistaken for a sparrow, but you can easily recognise it by the dark streaks on its breast. Look for it around the edges of woods and also in parks and gardens. It sits on a perch and swoops off to catch flies and other insects in mid-air. It nearly always returns to the same perch.

▲ The GOLDEN ORIOLE is one of Europe's most colourful birds, but it is rarely seen because it stays high in the trees for most of the time. It squeals loudly when alarmed and then sounds a bit like a cat. The bird is a summer visitor to most parts of Europe.

THE TAWNY OWL

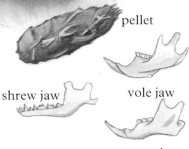

pellet

shrew jaw

vole jaw

mouse jaw

The tawny owl is the one with the well-known call of *too-wit-too-woo*. It also gives out a much louder *ki-wik* but, like all owls, it is completely silent when hunting. It is strictly nocturnal and it feeds mainly on mice and voles.

During the daytime the tawny owl rests on a branch close to the trunk of a tree. It's not easy to spot, but small birds might lead you to it. They often gather round the resting owl and make a lot of noise in an attempt to drive it away.

Owls all swallow their prey whole, but they can't digest the bones and fur. Some time after a meal the bones and fur are coughed out in a sausage-shaped bundle called an *owl pellet*. You can find the pellets underneath the owls' resting places, and if you pull them to pieces you can see exactly what the birds have been eating. The easiest bits to recognize are the lower jaws of the prey. Mice, voles, and shrews all have very different kinds of teeth.

THE BIRD THAT PLANTS FORESTS

The colourful JAY has a great liking for acorns. It collects them in the autumn and it can carry several at one time. It takes them from the woods and buries them in the surrounding fields. It eats some of them later, but it forgets where many of the acorns are and they start to grow. Jays may well have helped the oak forests to spread across Europe after the ice ages.

THE SPARROWHAWK

The SPARROWHAWK is one of the fastest and most agile birds in the woods. Using its long tail as a rudder, it can make amazing turns as it chases small birds through the trees and catches them in mid-air. When it has caught something it often takes it to a favourite perch to pluck it. Keep your eyes open for piles of feathers on rocks and tree stumps. You might be lucky enough to see the sparrowhawk return with another victim. Sparrowhawks are sometimes confused with kestrels (see p. 113) when in flight, but the kestrel has much more pointed wings.

sparrowhawk

kestrel

63

Loud noises, like rapid gun-fire, often frighten people in the woods, but it's only the GREAT SPOTTED WOODPECKER defending its territory. The bird hammers its beak rapidly against a dead branch to tell other woodpeckers that the territory is occupied. This is called *drumming*. An extra-strong skull ensures that the bird does not hurt itself. Woodpeckers also use their beaks to dig nest holes in the trees, and to dig insects from the wood. Dead trees are often full of holes made by the woodpeckers. If you watch one of these trees you might well see the birds at work. Look also for woodpecker workshops in bark crevices (see p. 57), where the birds open nuts.

green woodpecker

grey-headed woodpecker

✳

lesser spotted woodpecker

middle spotted woodpecker

✳

great-spotted woodpecker

Several kinds of woodpeckers live in the European forests, but they don't all drum. The green woodpecker feeds mainly on ants, which it digs from their nests in the ground.

The NUTHATCH is an agile bird that can walk down a tree trunk as easily as it walks up. Clinging tightly to the bark with its sharp claws, it searches for insects in the crevices.

The nuthatch nests in holes made by other birds. If a hole is too big the nuthatch makes it smaller by plastering mud around the outside.

The TREECREEPER looks a bit like a sparrow, but you can recognise it by its white front and curved beak. It uses its beak to probe for insects. The bird can only walk up the trunk, propping itself up by its stiff tail. When it gets to the top of the trunk it flies to the base of the next one and starts climbing again.

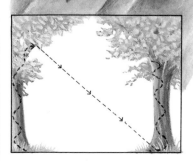

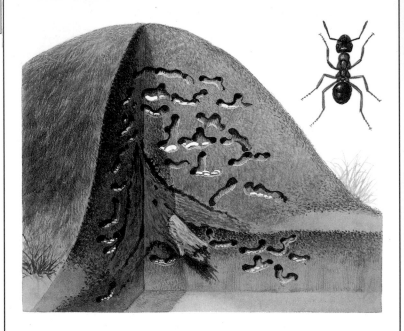

Wood ants build large mounds of soil and make their nests in them. They cover the mounds with leaves to keep the rain out. Millions of ants may live in a large nest, and their tiny feet make quite a noise as they tramp over the dead leaves on the ground. They eat huge numbers of caterpillars and other insects that would otherwise damage the trees. In some parts of Europe the ants are protected by law so that they can continue the good work.

BATTLING BEETLES

The male stag beetle's antlers are really enormous jaws, but he can't bite with them and he is quite harmless. He uses his antlers only for wrestling with other males. The strongest males win the females, which have normal-sized jaws.

► With its long legs, the
LOBSTER MOTH caterpillar
doesn't really look like a
caterpillar at all. It
frightens its enemies by
waving its legs about, and it
can also squirt a nasty
liquid at them. It feeds on
beech leaves.

◄ When alarmed, the PUSS
MOTH caterpillar puffs up
its front end and looks quite
fierce. This is enough to
frighten many of its
enemies. It also waves its
tails, which are really
specialized back legs, and it
can squirt a stinging liquid
from the front of its body.

WONDERFUL CAMOUFLAGE

Many insects rely on camouflage to hide them from
their enemies. Lots of caterpillars look like twigs.
Moths often look just like the bark on which they rest,
like the pale tussock moth in the picture below.

▼ The PURPLE EMPEROR is one of Europe's largest butterflies. Only the male has purple on its wings. The butterfly spends most of its time high in the trees, but it sometimes comes down to drink from puddles and even from animal dung. Like many other woodland butterflies, it gets most of its food from the sticky honeydew dropped by aphids. The caterpillar feeds on sallow leaves.

▶ The SPECKLED WOOD has cream spots in northern Europe, but in the south-west it has orange spots. The male sits in a patch of sunlight and chases off other males that try to land there. The caterpillar feeds on grasses.

◀ The COMMA looks as if it has been in a fight, but its ragged wings are quite natural. When it closes its wings it looks just like a dead leaf and birds take no notice of it. The caterpillar looks a bit like a bird dropping. It feeds on stinging nettles.

Blackberry bushes are good places for watching butterflies. Their nectar-filled blossom attracts several woodland species in the summer.

▶ The HOLLY BLUE is the only blue butterfly that you are likely to see in the trees. Its caterpillar feeds on the buds of holly and ivy.

◀ The RINGLET, easily identified by the pale rings on its underside, likes damp woodland. Unlike most butterflies, it will fly in very cloudy weather.

▶ The SILVER-WASHED FRITILLARY gets its name from the silvery streaks on the underside of its hind wings. Its caterpillar eats violet leaves.

◀ The WHITE ADMIRAL seems to fly effortlessly. It glides for long distances without flapping its wings, often flying in circles and returning to the same perch. Its caterpillar feeds on honeysuckle.

These odd-looking objects all grow on oak trees. They are called *galls* and they grow after tiny insects have laid their eggs on the trees. Each gall contains one or more insect grub. There are hundreds of different kinds of galls, each caused by a different insect, and you can find them on all sorts of plants.

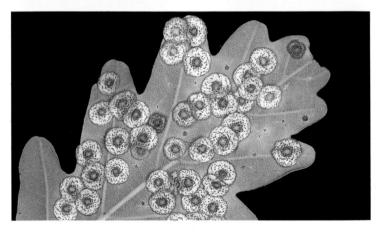

LIVING IN LEAVES

There's not a lot of room between the top and bottom surfaces of a leaf, but some insect grubs manage to live there. They chew their way through the leaf, leaving narrow tunnels called *leaf mines*. This mine in a bramble leaf was made by the caterpillar of a tiny moth.

In areas that get a lot of rain the woodland trees are often clothed with fluffy grey growths. Some hang down like beards, while others stand on the branches like miniature bushes. They are LICHENS, strange plants related to the fungi. Unlike the fungi, the lichens can make their own food and they don't harm the trees on which they grow. The lichen surface is rather powdery and the tiny grains of powder that blow away can grow into new lichens if they land in suitable places. Lichens can't stand dirty air and you won't find many of them on trees in and around large towns.

Many lichens grow like crusts on rocks and walls as well as on tree trunks. They grow slowly, but they can live for hundreds of years.

No-one has been scribbling on this tree trunk. The pale area is a sheet of lichen and the black scribbles are patches of spores that will grow into new lichens.

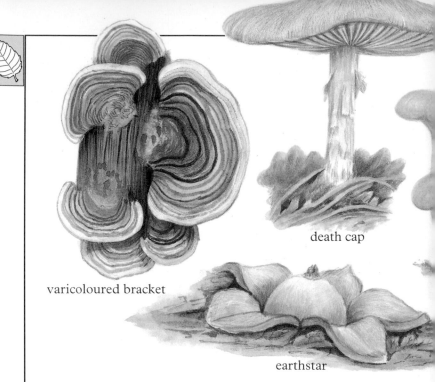

varicoloured bracket

death cap

earthstar

WOODLAND DECAY

As soon as the leaves fall from the trees in the autumn they are attacked by fungi and other microscopic forms of life. The fungi are in the form of slender living threads that work their way through the leaves. A single bucketful of dead leaves would contain miles of these threads, but most of them are much too thin for you to see. Juices from the threads gradually dissolve the leaves to provide food for the fungi.

When they have soaked up enough food the threads bunch tightly together to form the toadstools that grow up in the autumn. Some of the common woodland toadstools are pictured here. Without them, we would be up to our necks in dead leaves.

Some fungi also break down dead twigs and tree stumps, and some even attack the trees before they are dead. Their fine threads grow through the trunks and destroy the wood. They then produce special kinds of toadstools called *bracket fungi*, which grow from the trunks like little shelves.

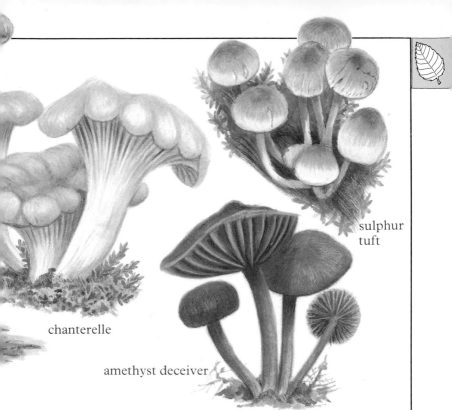

chanterelle

sulphur tuft

amethyst deceiver

FIRE SALAMANDER

The fire salamander got its name because people once thought that it was created in fires. The animals spend the day hiding in and under old logs. When people took the logs home to burn and put them on the fire, the salamanders used to crawl out. The bright colours warn predators to leave the salamander alone. Its skin is poisonous and stings the eyes and mouths of anything that attacks it.

*

THE GRASSLANDS

The grassy fields and hillsides around you are not really natural. The land was once covered with forest, and people gradually converted it to farmland. The trees were cut down and sheep and cattle began to graze over the land. New trees could not grow because the animals nibbled all the seedlings, so the land gradually became clothed with grass.

Much of the lowland grassland is broken up by walls or hedges to form small fields. These walls and hedgerows provide homes for all sorts of plants and animals and they are super places to explore at any time of the year.

FROM FIELD TO WOOD

If grazing stops for any reason the trees and bushes soon appear again, growing from seeds brought in by birds or by the wind. A field can become a wood again in less than 50 years. Many hillsides that were grazed until a few years ago are already covered with bushes.

STONE WALLS

Wherever there was a good supply of hard rock the farmers used to surround their fields with stone walls like these. The stones or slabs are not cemented together, but the builders fitted them together so cleverly that the walls hardly ever fall down. A good builder was able to build about six metres of wall in a day. It took a lot of men and time to build the thousands of kilometres of stone walls that you can see in Britain and several other parts of Europe.

Stone walls shelter sheep from the wind. This is important in upland areas.

The centre of the wall is often filled with soil, and the wind blows more soil and dust into the gaps between the stones. Lots of small plants, like this fern, grow in this soil.

Redstarts and other birds may nest in holes in the wall. In southern Europe you will find lizards scampering all over the walls and snapping up flies in the sunshine.

S ome hedges are hundreds of years old. Some of them are the remains of narrow strips of woodland that were left as boundaries along the roadsides or between villages. Others simply grew up on wasteland between neighbouring farms or villages. But many hedges were deliberately planted to enclose the fields. Over 320,000km of hedgerow were planted in Britain between 1750 and 1850. These new hedges are easy to recognise because they are usually straight and consist mainly of hawthorn bushes. Older hedges usually wriggle and they often have large stumps in them.

HOW OLD IS THAT HEDGE?

Hedge expert Max Hooper has discovered a simple way of finding out just how old some of our ancient hedges are. After studying hundreds of hedges, he discovered that the oldest hedges have the greatest variety of trees and shrubs in them. In fact, for every hundred years of its life a hedge seems to get an extra kind of tree or shrub. To find out the age of a hedge, count the number of different trees in a 30-metre stretch. If you find eight different kinds the hedge is likely to be about 800 years old. Five kinds will suggest an age of about 500 years. Don't count climbing shrubs like ivy, rose, and bramble.

L ots of flowers grow in the shelter of the hedge. If the hedge was part of an old wood there may be woodland flowers like bluebells and wood anemones. Hedges are important corridors. Plants and animals can spread along them from one wood to another.

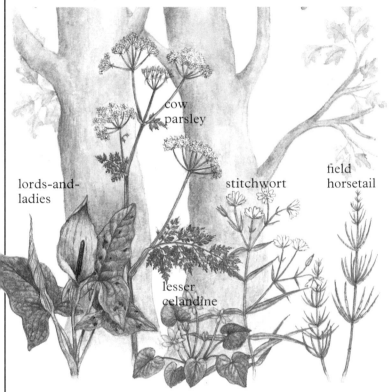

cow parsley

lords-and-ladies

stitchwort

field horsetail

lesser celandine

COW PARSLEY grows in nearly every roadside hedge. It is also called Queen Anne's lace because of its lace-like flowerheads.

STITCHWORT looks as if it has ten petals, but there are really only five. Each one is split down the middle.

The FIELD HORSETAIL is a relative of the ferns. It has no flowers. Its rough stems were used as pot scourers.

The LESSER CELANDINE has between five and twelve petals. Plants growing in deep shade produce few flowers. Instead, they have special buds that fall off and grow into new plants.

LORDS-AND-LADIES has an awful smell. It attracts lots of small flies. Later in the year it produces a spike of poisonous red berries.

flower

fruit

Hawthorn is one of the commonest hedgerow trees. The tree is also called quickthorn because it grows so quickly. You can grow your own hawthorns very easily by sticking some twigs in the ground. They will soon take root.

Hawthorn flowers have a very strong scent. They open in May.

Hawthorn fruits are called *haws*. Birds love them. They eat the flesh and spit out the seeds, so hawthorn springs up everywhere.

CHRIST'S THORN is a spiny bush of the Mediterranean area. It is often planted as a hedge to keep animals in and people out! Four other common hedgerow shrubs are pictured to the right.

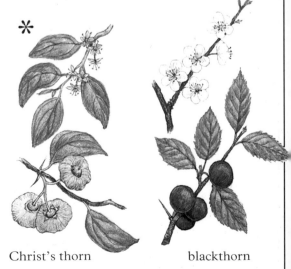

*

Christ's thorn

blackthorn

HEDGE REPAIRS

The hedge in the picture is being restored to good condition by the process called hedge-laying. This is used on old hedges which have become straggly and which have developed gaps in the bottom.

The hedge-layer cuts off the straggly branches to leave just the main stems. He then cuts part of the way through these stems, bends them over and fixes them in position with strong stakes. This work is done in the winter. Sturdy new shoots sprout from the stems in the spring and bind them into a strong hedge that will not let anything through.

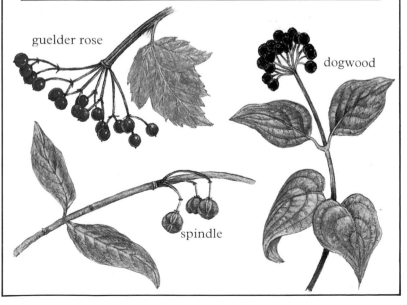

guelder rose

dogwood

spindle

These elm trees are dying. Their leaves are going yellow and whole branches have already died. They have been killed by a fungus called Dutch elm disease. Lots of elms have been killed by this disease in recent years.

elm bark beetle

◄ The bark of the dead trees is loose, and if you pull off a small piece you will find some strange patterns. These were made by the grubs of BARK BEETLES as they tunnelled between the bark and the wood. The fungus also lives in the tunnels and the beetles carry it from tree to tree.

◄ This oak tree is called a STAG-HEAD because of the dead, antler-like branches at the top. The tree might look as if it is dying, but you can see from the lush green foliage lower down that it is actually quite healthy. The dying back of the upper branches is natural in elderly oaks and some other trees. It gives new life and vigour to the lower parts. Stag-heads are found mainly in parks and hedgerows.

THE SMOTHERING IVY

The trunk of the tree below is completely covered with ivy. This climber takes minerals and water from the ground that would otherwise be taken up by the tree's roots. Its leaves also compete with those of the tree for light and air. An ivy-smothered tree will therefore not grow as well as one without ivy. But ivy does have its uses: many birds hide their nests in it and bats often roost in it.

Ivy flowers appear in the autumn and provide a rich feast of nectar for insects preparing for their winter sleep.

Ivy berries ripen in the spring.

The ivy has two kinds of leaves: dark, star-shaped ones on the bottom non-flowering shoots and shiny oval ones on the flowering shoots.

flower

berries

Pull an ivy shoot away from its support to see the tiny, sucker-like roots which hold it firmly in place on walls and tree trunks.

Climbers use other plants for support, so they don't need sturdy stems of their own. All their energy goes into growing quickly upwards into the sunlight. They use lots of ways of clinging to their neighbours.

▼ TRAVELLERS' JOY has curly leaf stalks which twist around neighbouring stems. This plant is also called old man's beard.

▲ WHITE BRYONY has spring-like tendrils which twine around other plants. They stretch easily and don't snap in the wind. This plant is very poisonous.

▶ HONEYSUCKLE simply twists around other branches, always in a clockwise direction. By partly strangling the branches it gives them a corkscrew shape.

▼ WILD ROSES and black-berries cling to their supports with their curved prickles.

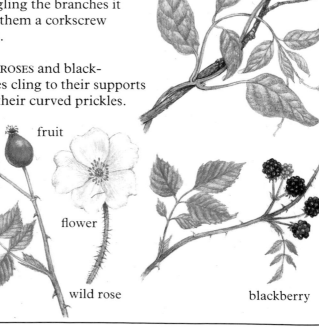

fruit

flower

wild rose

blackberry

With your magnifying glass you can easily make out the stinging hairs on the leaf or stem of a stinging nettle. Each hair has a swollen base, containing the poison, and a tiny glass-like bead at the tip. When you brush against one of these hairs you break off the fragile bead and uncover the sharp point. This pricks your skin and, because the hair is hollow, the poison flows into you from the base.

Stinging nettles are good to eat when cooked like spinach. The stinging hairs and the poison are destroyed during the cooking.

stinging nettle

flowers hang down in catkins

Roman nettle

The Roman nettle grows in southern Europe. Its female flowers form marble-like clusters.

NETTLES AND HISTORY

Stinging nettles can tell you something of the history of an area. They need lots of the mineral called phosphate, which is found in large quantities only where people have dumped or burned rubbish. So if you find a large patch of nettles you can be sure that the ground has been disturbed at some time. It could well be the site of an old building. Small patches of nettles spring up in fields and hedgerows where animals have dropped lots of dung.

The hedgehog is one of the easiest animals to recognize. With 5000 or more prickles for protection, it is less timid than many other animals and so it is also quite easy to watch. It is just as happy in the town as in the country. You can sometimes see the animal in the daytime, but it doesn't usually wake up until the evening. Then you can hear it grunting as it looks for food in the bottom of the hedge. It eats almost anything, but it is especially fond of beetles. It might eat 100 of them in a night, crunching them noisily with its sharp teeth. Most hedgehogs have regular routes, and they might walk three or four kilometres each night. They often come through our gardens. If you put out some cat food in the evenings they will stop for a meal every night. Then you can get a good look at them.

SEEING WITH EARS

Bats are a bit like mice with wings. The best time to see them is at dusk, when they are waking up and flying out to catch moths and other insects. They fly very fast, but they are very quiet. They use their ears to find their way about, although they are not actually blind as many people think.

All the time they are flying they send out high-pitched sounds. We can't normally hear them, but the bats' big ears can pick up the echoes bouncing back from trees and buildings. In this way, the bats can tell where things are and avoid bumping in to them, even on the darkest nights. Echoes bounce back from insects as well, and the bats can change course to catch them.

You won't see bats in the winter because there are not many insects for them to catch. They sleep all through the winter.

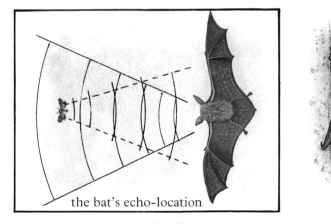

the bat's echo-location

Bats usually sleep hanging upside down in hollow trees and other dark places. They have to hang from their back legs because their front legs have been converted into wings.

HEDGEROW BIRDS

Fifty years ago there were no COLLARED DOVES in western Europe. Then, for some unknown reason, they spread rapidly from the east. Thousands now live in western Europe. You can see them on roadsides almost everywhere. Look for the thin black collar and listen for the distinctive call. It sounds a bit like a cuckoo, but there are three notes: *coo-coooo-coo*, with the middle one loud and long.

collared dove

dunnock

The DUNNOCK is also called the hedge sparrow, but it is not a real sparrow. It has a slender beak for eating insects. True sparrows have stout, seed-crushing beaks.

◄ The WREN is often mistaken for a mouse as it scuttles through the undergrowth in search of insects.

► The colourful GOLDFINCH is a seed-eater, but it doesn't always wait until the seeds are ripe. It often pulls flowers to pieces to get at the young seeds.

Look for the REDWING in the hedgerow in the winter. It is a cousin of the song thrush, but you can easily recognize it by the red patches on its sides and under its wings. The bird spends the summer in the north, but moves south for the winter. Large flocks roam the fields and hedgerows.

redwing

song thrush

fieldfare

The FIELDFARE is another winter visitor to Britain and southern Europe. It is easily identified by its grey head and rump. Fieldfares often join the redwings in the hedgerow. They will visit your garden if you put out a few apples.

The SLOW WORM isn't a worm and it isn't really slow. It is a legless lizard and it can move quite quickly when it has to, rather like a snake. Unlike snakes, the slow worm has eyelids and it can blink. Slow worms like damp grassland and are quite common in and around the ditches at the bottoms of hedgerows. A good way to find them is to turn over logs and stones, especially flat pieces. The slow worms like to hide under these because they get quite warm. They come out in the evening or after daytime showers to eat slugs. Slow worms are up to 50cm long.

The EUROPEAN GLASS LIZARD looks like a giant slow worm, up to 120cm long and 5cm thick. It looks like a snake, but it has eyelids like the slow worm. You can recognize the animal quite easily by the deep groove on each side of the body. It lives in dry, rocky places, including roadside walls, and feeds on insects and other creatures. It sometimes eats other lizards. The glass lizard is found only in south-east Europe.

HEDGEROW BUTTERFLIES

The HEDGE BROWN is also called the gatekeeper because it can nearly always be found flitting around sunny gaps and gateways in the hedge. It is especially fond of bramble blossom. Its caterpillar feeds on grasses on the sunny side of the hedge.

The LARGE SKIPPER likes to perch in the sun with its wings half open. Like all skipper butterflies, it darts rapidly from flower to flower. Its caterpillar feeds on grass and makes itself a little shelter by rolling a grass blade into a tube.

The WALL BROWN likes to bask on the ground at the bottom of a wall or hedge. You can find it throughout the summer. Like all members of the brown family, it tricks the birds with the eye-spots on its wings (see p. 109). Its caterpillar feeds on grasses.

The ORANGE TIP is a sure sign that spring has arrived. It is sometimes on the wing at the end of March in the south. Only the male has orange tips. The caterpillar eats the seed capsules of cuckooflower and similar plants.

wall brown

orange tip

large skipper

hedge brown

▼ Big fat BUMBLE BEES are among the first insects to appear in the spring. They are the queens and they have been sleeping all through the winter. After feasting on nectar from the spring flowers, they start looking for nest sites. Old mouse holes in the hedgebank suit them very well. When feeding their babies they take home lots of pollen. You can see big blobs of golden pollen stuck to their back legs.

► LEAF-CUTTER BEES make nests with pieces cut from leaves. They glue the pieces together to make sausage-shaped bags, which are then filled with pollen and nectar for the grubs. An egg is laid in each bag.

◄ CARPENTER BEES use their strong jaws to dig tunnels in wood. They lay their eggs there, in cells made from sawdust glued together with saliva.

Some bees make no nests. They lay their eggs in the nests of other kinds of bees, so they don't have to collect food for their grubs. They are called CUCKOO BEES.

The queen wasp sleeps through the winter, safely tucked up in a hollow tree or a shed or some other dry place. When she wakes up in the spring she must set to work to build her nest. She often builds in a hole under the hedge, and you can watch her searching for a suitable hole on sunny days. She builds her nest with paper, but she first has to make the paper. She scrapes wood from

The paper wasp makes a small umbrella-shaped nest.

common wasp's nest

dead trees and fences and you can often see her at work (see below). You can even hear her jaws scraping the wood. She chews the wood to pulp and uses this to make her fragile nest. After about two weeks the nest is about as big as a golf ball and contains 20–30 six-sided cells, each containing a wasp grub. When these grubs grow up they carry on building the nest. By mid-summer it can be as big as a football, with thousands of wasp grubs growing in it.

Thousands of spiders live in the hedgerow. You can see how many there are by looking at the hedge on an autumn morning, when the webs glisten with frost or dew.

◀ Not all spiders make webs. CRAB SPIDERS just sit in flowers or on leaves and pounce on any insects that land nearby. These spiders are often beautifully camouflaged and the insects don't see them until it's too late. Some crab spiders can change their colours to match different flowers.

▶ ORB-WEB SPIDERS make the well-known wheel-shaped webs with fine, strong silk from their bodies. Parts of the web are sticky and they trap insects that fly into them. The spider is careful not to walk on the sticky parts of the web when it eats the insects.

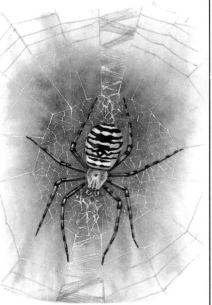

▼ Lots of spiders make HAMMOCK WEBS. These are almost flat sheets, but they usually sag when covered with dew. The spider lurks underneath. The webs are not sticky, but small insects get their feet tangled in the silk and the spider grabs them from below.

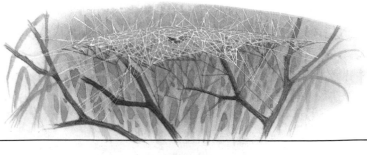

MISLEADING NAMES

▶ This fluffy growth on the wild rose is commonly called the ROBIN'S PINCUSHION, but it has nothing to do with robins. A tiny insect called a *gall wasp* pricks a rose bud or a young leaf in the spring and lays her eggs in it. The area then swells up to form the growth, with the baby gall wasps feeding happily inside it. Growths caused by insects in this way are called *galls*. You can see some others on page 70.

▶ The SCORPION FLY gets its name because the male's tail turns up like that of a scorpion, but it is a harmless insect. It feeds on over-ripe fruit, dead insects, and other rotting matter.

◀ The little blobs of froth that we see on plants in the spring are generally known as CUCKOO-SPIT. Each blob is made by the baby of an insect called a *frog-hopper*. It lives in the middle of the froth and sucks juices from the plant. People used to think that the froth had something to do with cuckoos because it appears at about the same time as the cuckoo.

FIELDS AND MEADOWS

Have a good look at the fields when you next go on a journey. You'll see lots of crops, but many fields will just be full of grass. Whether the farmers grow crops or grass depends largely on the climate. Cereals don't ripen well in the cooler and wetter areas. But grass does grow well in these places, so the farmers can use it to rear sheep and cattle. Fields where animals graze regularly are called *pastures*. The grass is short. Meadows are fields where the grass is allowed to grow tall in the summer. It is then cut to make hay, for feeding the animals in the winter.

In the past, meadows were full of wild flowers in the summer, but you won't find many flower-filled meadows today. Farmers plough their meadows every few years and sow special grass seed to produce big hay crops.

The steeper hillsides can't be ploughed. Sheep often graze on them, but there are still plenty of flowers. These areas are called rough grazings and often lack walls or hedges.

Some of the best wild flower meadows are high in the mountains, especially in the Alps and in the mountains of Spain. These meadows have never been

ploughed and hundreds of different kinds of flowers grow there, as you can see in the pictures below and opposite. The meadows are cut for hay every few years, but this does not harm the flowers.

Grasses are wonderful plants. They don't mind being grazed or trodden on or even cut with a lawn mower. They just keep on growing from the base. Not many other plants can grow like this. Without the grasses we would have no lawns or playing fields. More importantly, there would be no sheep or cattle to provide us with food.

There are lots of different kinds of grasses. Some like dry soils and others like damp soils. Some form mats that link up to form turf, while others form clumps or tussocks. Flower heads push up in the summer. They are usually green or brown and they have no petals or scent. They just scatter their pollen in the wind. You can identify

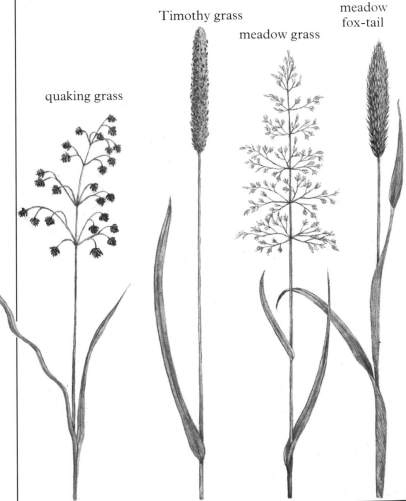

quaking grass

Timothy grass

meadow grass

meadow fox-tail

some of the common grasses by the shape of the flower head. Some heads are loosely branched, while others form dense spikes like little ears of wheat.

COCK'S-FOOT grass has a flower head shaped a bit like a chicken's foot, while the various kinds of meadow grasses have flower hcads shaped like miniature Christmas trees. FEATHER GRASS, which grows in the Alps, has long feathery growths which carry its seeds away. By coiling and uncoiling as the weather changes, the feathers actually screw the seeds into the ground.

This magnified grass flower shows how the stamens hang out and scatter pollen. Some of the pollen is caught by the stigmas of other flowers, and then seeds can start to form.

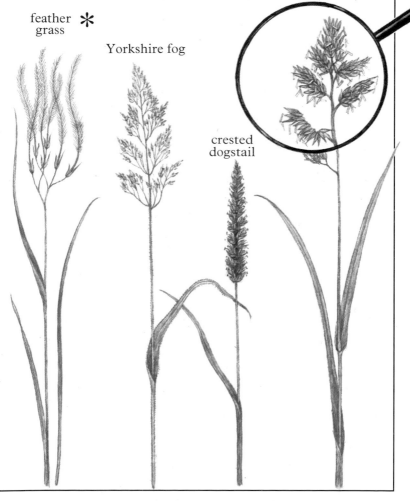

cock's foot grass

feather * grass

Yorkshire fog

crested dogstail

GRASSLAND FLOWERS

Grassy hillsides, as long as they are not grazed too heavily, are covered with wild flowers. The flowers die out if there is too much grazing. They also suffer if there is not enough grazing, because the grasses grow tall then and smother many of the smaller flowers. Bushes also start to grow if there is no grazing.

▶ YELLOW RATTLE gets its name because the ripe seeds rattle inside their capsules.

▼ The STEMLESS THISTLE has a beautiful flower, but its spiny leaves always seem to grow just where you want to sit for your picnic.

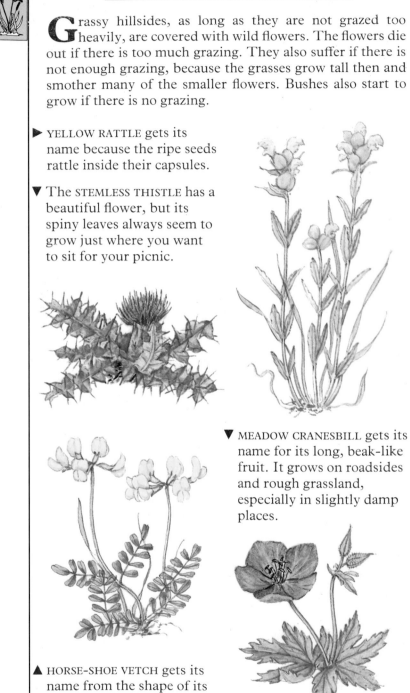

▼ MEADOW CRANESBILL gets its name for its long, beak-like fruit. It grows on roadsides and rough grassland, especially in slightly damp places.

▲ HORSE-SHOE VETCH gets its name from the shape of its fruits, which look like chains of tiny horse-shoes.

▼ WOAD grows on rough hillsides and roadsides, mainly in southern Europe. Its leaves produce a blue dye, which the Ancient Britons used to paint on their bodies.

▲ The PASQUE FLOWER is one of the first to open on the grassland in the spring. Its name comes from an old word meaning Easter, which is when it usually flowers.

◄ The COWSLIP is the grassland cousin of the primrose. People used to make wine from the flowers and drink it to cure sleeplessness.

► BIRD'S-FOOT TREFOIL gets its name because its pods spread out like the toes of a bird. Trefoil means three-leaved and refers to the three lobes of each leaf.

◀ The BULBOUS BUTTERCUP likes dry grassland. Its sepals bend sharply back under the flower. The underground part of its stem is swollen rather like a bulb. The MEADOW BUTTERCUP likes damper grassland and its sepals do not bend back.

▶ The ROCKROSE is not a rose at all, although its flower is a bit like a rose. It forms little cushions in rough grassland and often grows on ant-hills. Each flower lasts for just a few hours.

▼ The SNAKE'S HEAD FRITILLARY grows mainly in riverside meadows which have never been ploughed. It gets its name because the drooping flower buds look like snakes' heads.

▲ AGRIMONY grows in all sorts of grassland. Its little fruits are covered with hooks which catch in your socks and clothing when you walk through the grass.

WILD ORCHIDS

You might think that all orchids come from hot countries or greenhouses, but quite a lot live in the countryside around us. They are not as big and colourful as the tropical ones, but they are just as interesting. The flower of the BEE ORCHID plays tricks on bumble bees. It looks and smells just like a female bumble bee. Male bees try to mate with it, but all they manage to do is to pollinate the flower – which is just what the orchid wants!

lady orchid

bee orchid

monkey orchid

The flower of the LADY ORCHID looks like a lady in a long skirt and a bonnet.

The MONKEY ORCHID has bent 'arms' and 'legs', rather like a monkey.

The MAN ORCHID got its name because the flower has two 'arms' and 'legs'.

man orchid

This insect exploring at the mouth of its burrow is a female FIELD CRICKET. She is listening for the song of a male. This song is like a shrill whistle and the male actually makes it by rubbing his wings together. Parts of the wings start to vibrate rapidly and they produce the sound – just as a vibrating violin string gives out a sound. The song is quite musical and some people actually keep field crickets in cages instead of canaries!

When the female hears the male's song she crawls towards him and moves into his burrow. The insects mate there and the female lays her eggs in the surrounding soil. The eggs hatch quickly, but the baby crickets take a whole year to grow up. They feed mainly on grass and other plants but, like other crickets, they also eat aphids and other small insects.

Listen for the field cricket's song in early summer.

Male grasshoppers sing by rubbing their big back legs against their wings. A row of tiny teeth on each leg knocks against a hard ridge on the wing and sets up the vibrations which cause the sound. It's rather like drawing the teeth of a comb over the edge of a piece of paper. Each kind of grasshopper has its own special song. You can keep grasshoppers very easily in a cage if you give them fresh grass every day.

► The DARK BUSH CRICKET lives in hedges and other rough places, where it nibbles leaves and eats other small insects. Listen for the male's song in summer and autumn. You will hear it mainly in the afternoon and evening. It is a short hiss, repeated every few seconds. The male makes the sound by rubbing his tiny saddle-like wings together.

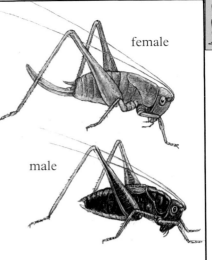

female

male

◄ Most grasshoppers are well camouflaged in the grass, like this MEADOW GRASS-HOPPER. Most can fly, but the meadow grasshopper's wings are too short and it has to make do with hopping on its big back legs.

► The BLUE-WINGED GRASSHOPPER is easily mistaken for a butterfly when it flashes its bright blue hind wings in flight. But then it drops to the ground and is hard to find. Some have red hind wings.

*

▶ The GLOW-WORM isn't a
▼ worm at all. It is a small
brown beetle. The female
has no wings and looks a bit
like a woodlouse. She sits in
the grass and switches on
her pale green light on
summer nights. The male
can fly and he zooms over
the grassland looking for
female lights. When he sees
one he drops down to mate
with the female.

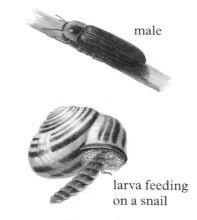

male

larva feeding
on a snail

The FIREFLY is another
beetle. It is closely related
to the glow-worm, but
males and females both
carry lanterns. The male
flies after dark and flashes
his light every second. The
female has wings, but she
doesn't fly. She sits
patiently in the grass until
she sees a male flashing his
light above her. Then she
flashes her own light to
guide him down. Fireflies
live in parts of southern
Europe, and their flashing
lights are almost like
firework displays.

*

THE REFUSE COLLECTORS *

This colourful beetle has a most important and useful job in the countryside. It buries dead birds and other small animals. Male and female beetles work together, and when they have buried the body the female lays her eggs on it. When the eggs hatch the young beetles feed on the rotting flesh.

▲ Many beetles clear away cow-pats and other animal droppings. They are called DUNG BEETLES. Some, like these scarabs from southern Europe, roll balls of dung over the ground and bury them. The females then lay their eggs in the dung. Imagine what the country-side would be like without the work of the dung beetles!

THE BEETLE WITH A NOSE-BLEED

This clumsy, fat beetle is called the BLOODY-NOSED BEETLE, and if you pick one up you might find out why. A drop of bright red blood will probably ooze from around its mouth. But the beetle is not hurt. This is simply the insect's way of protecting itself. The

sudden appearance of the blood frightens any bird that tries to peck the beetle.

105

GRASSLAND BUTTERFLIES

Lots of butterflies live on the grasslands. The adults feed on nectar from the flowers, while their caterpillars nibble the leaves of the grasses and many other plants.

The SMALL HEATH is one of Europe's commonest butterflies. It always rests with its wings closed.

The male and female of the COMMON BLUE look so different that they are often thought to be different species. Many kinds of blue butterflies live on the grasslands of Europe.

The CLOUDED YELLOW is a great traveller. Every spring it flies north from its home in southern Europe.

marbled white

black-veined white

six-spot burnet moth

small copper

The MARBLED WHITE is a member of the brown family. You can see this by the eye-spots around its wings (see p. 109).

The DARK GREEN FRITILLARY loves to feed at thistle flowers. You can recognise it by its large size and by the green and silver spots on the underside.

The BLACK-VEINED WHITE can often be seen drinking from puddles.

The SMALL COPPER often chooses a particular flower as a perch and returns to it time and time again during the day. It chases other butterflies away.

The SIX-SPOT BURNET MOTH is often mistaken for a butterfly because it is brightly coloured and flies by day, but butterflies don't fold their wings over their bodies in this way.

clouded yellow

dark green fritillary

common blue

small heath

BEWARE OF THE POISON

This is the message given out by all of these brightly coloured insects. The bold colours are a warning to birds that they taste nasty. Some of them are actually poisonous. Young birds will try them, but they soon learn their lesson. After that they leave them alone.

six-spot burnet moth   cinnabar moth   froghopper

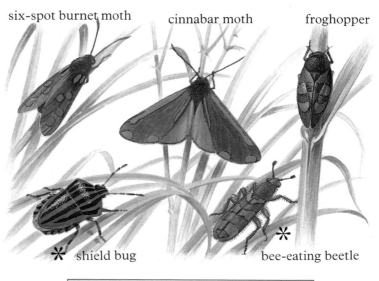

* shield bug   bee-eating beetle *

A BIT OF TRICKERY

Only one of these insects is a wasp – the top one. The other is a hover-fly. If you look carefully you will see that its wings and feelers are quite different from those of the wasp. The wasp's black and yellow coat warns that it is unpleasant. Birds learn to leave wasps alone just as they learn to leave the red and black insects alone. The hover-fly is not unpleasant, but birds still leave it alone because it looks rather like a wasp. This kind of trickery is called mimicry. We say that the hover-fly *mimics* or copies the wasp. Lots of harmless insects are protected because they look like stinging bees and wasps.

THE MANTIS SAYS GRACE

The PRAYING MANTIS is quite common in grassy and bushy places in the southern half of Europe. It got its name because, when it holds its front legs in front of its face, it resembles someone saying prayers. Saying grace would be an even better description, because the front legs are vicious traps waiting to grab the next meal. When another insect comes along the spiky legs shoot out with great speed and accuracy to catch it. There is no escape from the sharp spines and the mantis's strong jaws quickly get to work to chew up the victim. The mantis is well camouflaged amongst the vegetation.

NOW YOU SEE ME, NOW YOU DON'T

When a MEADOW BROWN butterfly lands it shows the eye-like spots on its wing-tips for a few seconds. If nothing attacks it in this time, the butterfly feels safe and settles down to rest. It pulls its wings down and hides the eye-spots. The butterfly is then very hard to find.

The eye-spots of the meadow brown are part of the insect's survival kit, designed to fool the birds. They draw the birds' attention away from the head and the real eyes. When a bird attacks the eye-spots the most it gets is a little piece of wing.

The SKYLARK is more often heard than seen. It sings its shrill warbling song while hovering high in the sky. All you can usually see is a dark speck. The bird nests on the ground and always keeps well away from trees and hedges. Large flocks roam the fields in autumn and winter in search of seeds and insects.

The YELLOWHAMMER gets its name from its bright yellow head. It likes to hunt for seeds and insects in rough grassland, where there are plenty of hedges or bushes from which it can sing. Some people think that its twittering song, with a long final note, sounds like *a little bit of bread and no cheese*.

A pile of broken shells around a large stone will tell you that a SONG THRUSH has been at work. The bird loves to eat snails, which it bashes on a stone until the shells break. It makes a surprisingly loud noise as it does this. Each bird has a number of favourite stones, which are called *anvils*. They are scattered through its territory and you can find them in the gardens as well as in the countryside.

THE CLEVER CROWS

Members of the crow family are sturdy birds with large beaks. They eat almost anything. You will often see them feeding on rabbits and other animals that have been killed on the road. Crows are quick to learn and they are among the cleverest of birds.

hooded crow

carrion crow

rook

Look for ROOKS building their nest colonies, or *rookeries*, in the tree tops early in the spring. The birds roam the fields in large flocks in search of grain and insects. You can easily recognize a rook by the grey patch on its face and by the dense feathers at the tops of its legs, like a pair of shorts.

The CARRION CROW looks like a rook, but it has no grey on its face and no 'shorts'. In Ireland and in most parts of northern and eastern Europe it is replaced by the closely related HOODED CROW, which has a grey body. Like the rook, they nest in tree tops.

► The MAGPIE is often called a thief because, for some unknown reason, it takes brightly coloured objects to decorate its nest. Coins, jewellery, and milk bottle tops have all been found in its nest. Like the carrion crow, the magpie often eats the eggs and nestlings of other birds.

MILLIONS OF STARLINGS

The starling is one of the world's commonest birds. You can see thousands on winter afternoons, when they fly in from all directions to sleep in a wood or in a town. They use the same place every night and they make an awful mess with their droppings. They also make an awful noise as they settle down for the night. In the morning they fly off in small groups to look for insects and other small creatures. They also visit our gardens and pinch all the food from our bird tables. The flocks break up in the spring, when the birds are ready to nest.

THE ELEGANT LAPWING

The lapwing is also called the peewit, because that's exactly what its call sounds like. In some places it is called the butcher bird, because its white underside resembles a traditional butcher's apron. Look for lapwing flocks strutting over the ploughed fields in the autumn. They are searching for worms and insects.

SHARP-EYED HUNTERS

▲ The KESTREL spends a lot of time hovering, with its tail feathers spread like a fan. It is studying the ground carefully, looking for the slightest movement that might betray a vole or a mouse or even a beetle. The bird plunges down whenever it sees something, and if it is lucky it comes up with its next meal in its talons. Look for kestrels on a car journey. Lots of them hunt over roadsides and motorway verges.

▼ The LITTLE OWL is one of Europe's smallest owls. It likes farmland and other open country, and it hunts by day as well as by night. Look for it on fence posts and hedgerow trees. Look for pellets under the perch (see p. 62).

◄ The SHORT-EARED OWL has such short ear tufts that you can't usually see them at all! It is a daytime hunter and is often mistaken for a hawk. Most owls watch for prey from perches, but the short-eared owl hunts on the wing. It glides slowly over the grass and pounces on any small animal that it sees or hears.

RABBITS AND HARES

Do you know the difference between a rabbit and a hare? Lots of people muddle them up. A hare is generally bigger and it has longer legs and ears. But this doesn't help if you can see only one animal.

Look closely at the ears. Hares' ears have black tips. There are two kinds of hares, the brown hare and the mountain hare. The latter usually turns white for the winter, but it still keeps its black ear-tips.

mountain hare

rabbit

brown hare

rabbit track

WEASELS AND STOATS

Here are two more animals that are easily confused. Both are fierce meat-eaters, catching birds and other small animals, including rabbits, by day and by night. You will most often see them dashing across roads and footpaths. The stoat is larger than the

weasel as a rule and it always has a black tip to its tail. In the north the stoat turns white for the winter.

weasel

stoat

These furry little creatures are common in fields and hedgerows, but they usually keep out of sight. They belong to a group called *rodents*. They are gnawing animals and they feed mainly on plants. Their front teeth are like chisels for cutting through the stems. Their back teeth are almost flat and are used for grinding the food. Voles are active during both day and night. You can often find their narrow runs snaking through the long grass. Mice are mainly nocturnal. They have bigger eyes and ears than voles, more pointed snouts and longer tails.

harvest mouse

woodmouse

common shrew

field vole

bank vole

SHREWS

Shrews are easily recognized by their long snouts. They are not related to the mice and voles. They feed on worms, insects, and other small animals, which they slice up with their sharp teeth.

You can hear shrews squeaking in the vegetation by day and by night. Like the mice and voles, the shrews have lots of enemies, including owls and kestrels. The jaws of all three animals are on p. 62.

SNAKES IN THE GRASS

Snakes are warmth-loving animals, and spend a lot of time sun-bathing. Most of Europe's 27 different kinds live in the south. Only three live in the British Isles, and none lives in Ireland. Snakes are generally active by day, although some hunt by night as well in the south. They all go into a deep sleep for the winter. Snakes are all flesh-eaters and they find their food mainly by smell. They continually flick their tongues out to pick up scents.

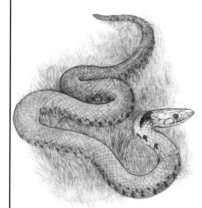

◄ The GRASS SNAKE is usually recognised by its yellow collar. It is a good swimmer and often lives by water. Frogs make up much of its diet. The grass snake is harmless to us, but if you pick it up it may give out an awful smell.

► The ADDER or VIPER is the only poisonous snake in the northern half of Europe. You can generally recognise it by the dark zig-zag pattern on its back. It feeds mainly on small mammals. It has several close relatives in southern Europe.

◄ The WESTERN WHIP SNAKE is one of the longest snakes in Europe, sometimes reaching lengths of two metres. It lives in both wet and dry grasslands and feeds on all sorts of animals, including other snakes. It bites fiercely if handled, but it is not poisonous.

*

Lots of different kinds of toadstools grow in rings – in the fields and woods and even on people's lawns. For a long time people thought that the rings were connected with fairies and their dances, so they were called fairy rings. Some people even thought that they were produced by lightning, but we now know the real explanation.

Toadstools spring from clusters of fluffy threads that feed on decaying matter in the ground. As it grows, the cluster spreads out in all directions, but it soon uses up all the food in the middle. The threads in the middle then die, leaving just a ring around the outside. The next crop of toadstools comes up in a small ring. The underground threads keep on growing, and they have to keep on pushing outwards to find food. So the ring gets bigger every year. Some rings are more than 50m across and probably several hundred years old.

Some common ring-forming toadstools.

parasol mushroom

giant puffball

horse mushroom

THE HEATHLANDS

Heathlands occur mainly in the lowlands, and if you dig into the soil you will find that it is always sandy. The heathlands were once covered with trees, but when people cut them down to make way for farming, they found that the soil was not good enough for their crops. They abandoned the land and the heathers soon spread over it. Heathers like poor, sandy soil. Many areas have stayed as heathland ever since, because grazing animals and fires have not allowed trees to grow again. But trees have grown up on some heathlands and turned them back to forests. The first tree to invade the heathland is usually the birch (see p. 26), which actually improves the heathland soil so that pines and other trees can follow.

EXPLORING HEATHLANDS

The heathlands are great places for exploring in the summer holidays. The purple heathers are in full flower and bees jostle each other as they queue up to suck nectar from them. Keep your eyes open and you will see lots of other interesting plants and animals on the heathland.

WHICH HEATHER IS WHICH?

The heathers are the commonest plants on the heathland. Their roots are better than those of most other plants at getting food from the poor soil.

▶ COMMON HEATHER, or LING, grows all over the heathland. Its tiny leaves hug the stems. The pale purple flowers are star-like when they are fully open. Heather doesn't mind being grazed or even burned. New shoots quickly spring up.

▼ BELL HEATHER grows on the driest parts of the heathland. Its flowers are like little pink bells. The leaves are like tiny pins and they grow in threes.

▲ CROSS-LEAVED HEATH gets its name because its greyish leaves grow in fours, forming little crosses around the stems. Its flowers are paler than those of bell heather and they look more like tiny eggs. It grows in the wettest areas.

Gorse can be seen in flower at any time of the year, even in the middle of winter. But it is at its best in the spring, when it turns many heathlands yellow with its sweetly scented flowers. Gorse is a noisy plant in the summer, when its ripe pods explode and shoot out their seeds with loud popping sounds. The spines are actually the plant's leaves. Animals eat them when they are young and tender, but keep well away from the older spines.

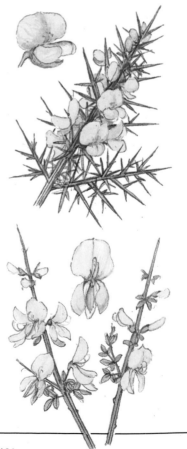

▶ BROOM is a cousin of the gorse, but it has no spines. It grows on sand dunes by the sea as well as on heathland. The plant's stems were often made into brooms for sweeping.

▶ The DODDER is a really weird plant. It is a parasite that steals its food from its neighbours. It has no leaves or roots and its stems are like strands of pink or yellow cotton. These stems twine around other plants and push tiny suckers into them to steal the food. When it has stolen enough food, the dodder produces bunches of tiny pink flowers. Look for the dodder on the heathland in

the summer. You will find it mainly on heather and gorse.

▲ The SUNDEW is a murderous plant. It catches and eats the insects that are attracted to its sparkling leaves. The shiny blobs on the leaves are very sticky and there is no escape for an insect that lands on them. The leaf gradually closes around the trapped insect and digests it. This takes a few days, then the leaf opens again ready for the next meal. Look for sundews on the damper parts of the heath.

BIRDS OF THE HEATHLAND

The HOBBY is an expert flier. It catches other birds in mid-air. It even catches bats and dragonflies. Courting birds perform spectacular air-shows, with the male often handing food to the female as they fly past each other at high speed.

The RED-BACKED SHRIKE perches on bushes waiting for prey and darts off to catch insects and lizards. It is sometimes called the butcher bird because it hangs its victims on thorns or barbed wire – just as a butcher hangs meat on hooks.

The STONECHAT gets its name because its call sounds like someone bashing two stones together. Look and listen for the bird in bushy areas. It often calls from the tops of gorse bushes, flicking its wings and tail at the same time.

FAST AND FIERCE

The GREEN TIGER BEETLE is one of the fastest and fiercest of insects. It makes a loud buzzing sound as it zooms over the heathland, but it is harmless to us. On the ground it can run at speeds of about 60cm per second as it chases ants and other insects and catches them in its huge, spiky jaws. This is equivalent to a man running 100m in a second – ten times faster than an Olympic sprinter!

The young tiger beetle is less energetic. It sits at the mouth of a burrow and uses its jaws to grab any insect that walks by. It takes the victim to the bottom of the burrow and eats it.

SUN-LOVING LIZARDS

Lizards spend a lot of time basking in the sunshine. If they don't keep themselves warm they can't run fast enough to escape from their enemies. Lots of birds and snakes like to eat lizards. Sometimes a lizard is not quick enough and it gets caught by the tail, but it can snap off its tail and carry on running. The lizard eventually grows a new tail.

Lots of butterflies and moths visit the heathland in summer, but few of them live there all the time. Not many caterpillars can digest the leaves of the heather and other heathland plants.

▲ Male EMPEROR MOTHS fly
◀ rapidly over the heathland. Their large antennae help them to pick up the scent of the females from as much as two kilometres away. The females are greyer than the males and have small antennae. The caterpillars feed on heather and many other plants.

▶ The GRAYLING BUTTERFLY is an expert at camouflage. It is very hard to spot when it settles on the ground and leans over towards the sun. It lives on dry grasslands as well as on heathland.

◀ The SILVER-STUDDED BLUE BUTTERFLY gets its name from the tiny silvery spots on its underside. It lives in all kinds of grassy places in most of Europe. Its caterpillar feeds on heather and gorse and many other plants.

THE WASP'S NURSERY

This wasp is stocking up the nursery for her baby. She is a POTTER WASP. She builds her vase-shaped nursery with clay, using her jaws and front legs as tools. When it is complete she lays an egg in it and fills it with caterpillars, which she paralyses with her sting. She then seals it up and goes off to make another one. Look for the little nests on the heather stalks.

THE WASP THAT KILLS BEES

The BEE-KILLER WASP is carrying a honey bee back to its nest. The bee can't move because it has been paralysed by the wasp's sting. The wasp packs several bees into its underground nest with its eggs. When the eggs hatch the baby wasps feed on the stored bees. Bee-killers destroy whole colonies of honey bees in some places. They are rare in Britain.

MOUNTAIN AND MOORLAND

As you climb a mountain the air gradually gets colder. Deciduous trees give way to firs and other conifers. The highest slopes are too cold and windy even for these trees to grow. This is the alpine zone. It is not an easy place to explore, but if you are lucky enough to make a car journey through the Alps or Pyrenees you will be able to see something of the alpine plants and animals without too much trouble.

The very highest slopes are permanently covered with snow, but where the snow melts you can find some beautiful plants. Most of them are very small because, with the short growing season, they can add only a little bit each year.

THE TREE LINE

The level at which trees stop growing on a mountain is called the tree line. You can see it very clearly on some mountains. On the south-facing slopes of the Alps it is about 1800 metres above sea level. On the north-facing slopes it is about 300 metres lower.

WEARING DOWN THE MOUNTAINS

Mountains are formed when immense earthquakes buckle the earth's crust and push it up into great ridges. But as soon as the mountains have been pushed up, the weather starts to wear them down again. Rain gets into little cracks in the rocks, and when it freezes it expands with such force that it cracks the rocks even more. Pieces break away and tumble down the slopes. This is called *frost shattering* and it is most obvious on higher slopes.

The broken pieces pile up on the mountainsides to form loose banks like those in the picture. These banks are called *screes*.

Rainwater and melted snow rushing down the slopes continue the process of erosion by washing stones and boulders into the streams. The streams carry the stones away, and so cut further into the rocks. After many millions of years the mountain will eventually disappear.

Young mountains are high and rugged.
Older mountains are low and smoother.

SHAPED BY THE RAIN

This curious pillar in the French Alps has been produced by the rain. Look closely and you will see that it is made of boulder clay – a mixture of stones and boulders embedded in soft clay. For hundreds of years the large boulder at the top of the pillar has acted like an umbrella, protecting the clay underneath it while the surrounding clay has been washed away by the rain. The boulder will eventually fall and then the pillar will become pointed as it is gradually worn away by the rain. Pillars of this kind are called earth pillars and they generally occur in mountain valleys where they are protected from strong winds.

Most of the plants of the alpine zone form cushions or mats close to the ground, where their leaves are protected from the cold, drying winds. They usually open their flowers as soon as the snow has gone. If they didn't, they might not have time to ripen and scatter their seeds before the snow returns.

◀ EDELWEISS is one of the most famous of Europe's mountain flowers. Its furry coat prevents it from drying up in the cold winds.

▼ The ALPINE SNOWBELL forms purple carpets on flat, wet areas. It can hardly wait to open its flowers and often pushes them up before the snow has completely melted.

▼ ACANTHUS-LEAVED CARLINE THISTLE is one of the biggest mountain flowers. It is up to 15cm across, but it has no stem and it sits directly on the ground surrounded by its large prickly leaves. It is most common in open areas just below the tree line. The dead flower heads are popular ornaments.

▲ The ALPENROSE is not really a rose: it is a member of the heather family. It is one of the largest plants in the alpine zone, often forming big clumps in the shelter of boulders.

▲ The TRUMPET GENTIAN is one of several similar deep blue flowers growing in grassy places in the alpine zone. Several other gentians have bright blue star-shaped flowers.

▲ GLACIER CROWFOOT is a white buttercup that grows high in the mountains, often on stony ground close to snow patches.

▲ HOUSELEEKS cover rocky outcrops with their rosettes of tightly-packed juicy leaves. Their roots grow into the tiniest cracks and hold the plants firmly in place. The cobweb houseleek's leaves are clothed with cobweb-like hairs.

golden eagle

raven

BIRDS OF THE MOUNTAINS

You can see some really big birds in the mountains. You won't see many small ones. They would be blown away or smashed against the rocks by the strong winds, but the bigger birds enjoy the wind and they put on spectacular displays of soaring and diving around the rock faces.

The LAMMERGEIER is Europe's biggest mountain bird. It is over 100cm long. It is also called the bearded vulture because of the tuft of black feathers around its beak. It feeds on dead animals and even knows how to get at the marrow inside their bones: it carries the bones into the air and drops them on to the rocks until they break.

The GOLDEN EAGLE gets its name for the golden brown feathers on its head and neck. It soars round the mountain tops for hours as it searches for hares and other animals below.

The RAVEN is the biggest member of the crow family, up to 65cm long. Look for the diamond-shaped tail to identify the bird as it tumbles and swoops through the air. It can even fly upside-down for short distances.

The CHOUGH is another kind of crow. It gets its

lammergeier

chough

name, pronounced *chuff*, because its call sounds just like that. It is easily recognized by its long red beak. You can see it swooping and gliding around coastal cliffs or mountain crags. The Alpine chough has a shorter yellow beak.

The WALLCREEPER is one of the few small birds that can survive high in the mountains. It usually keeps close to the rock faces in sheltered gorges, where it feeds on insects. Look for the flashes of its pink wings as it flutters from rock to rock. The bird has to move lower down in the winter because it can't find insects in the snow.

wallcreeper

*

The ALPINE MARMOT is a ground-living squirrel. With no trees to climb, it does not need a bushy tail for balance. It lives on grassy and rocky slopes, generally above 2000 metres, and feeds on a wide range of plants. The animals live in small family groups. Each group has a deep, hay-filled burrow. Marmots are shy and the best way to see them is to find a burrow and watch it with binoculars from a distance. You will see the animals scampering over the grass, sitting up every now and then to look for danger. If they are alarmed, by an eagle soaring overhead perhaps, they give out sharp whistles which send the other marmots scurrying back to their burrows. The marmots sleep for between six and eight months of the year, snuggly tucked up in the hay at the bottom of their burrows.

marmots' burrows

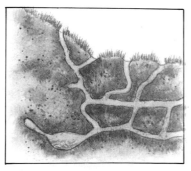

◄ The CHAMOIS is an elegant and sure-footed animal that lives in most of Europe's mountainous regions. It can climb the steepest slopes and it makes amazing leaps from rock to rock. Up to 80cm tall at the shoulder, it is a bit like a goat and a bit like an antelope. Small herds graze above the tree line in the summer, but they won't let you get very close to them. They move down into the forests in the winter, when their coats become darker.

▼ The ALPINE IBEX is a mountain goat that lives high in the Alps. The female has much shorter horns than the male pictured here. The animals live in small herds and stay above the tree line all year.

They scrape the snow away with their hooves to get at the plants underneath. The Spanish ibex, which lives in the Pyrenees, is similar but its horns are smoother and they curve upwards and outwards.

Spanish ibex

Moorland is covered with heather and grass like heath-land, but it develops in cool areas with lots of rain – usually in upland areas. There is usually a thick layer of peat under the vegetation and this makes many moorlands rather squelchy places. Huge areas of Scotland are covered with this kind of moorland. It is called blanket bog because it covers everything. There is a lot of the spongy moss called *Sphagnum*. It is this that makes most of the peat.

digging peat

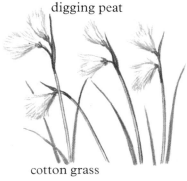

cotton grass

Some moors have always been moorland, but tree trunks discovered in the peat in other places show that some moors were once covered with trees. A change to a wetter climate caused these old woods to deteriorate and change into moorland. Today's moorlands provide peat for fuel, and many are also grazed by sheep and grouse. The grazing moors are burnt every few years to encourage the growth of tender new shoots for the animals.

▼ The CURLEW gets its name from its call of *curlee-curlee*, which you can hear all over the moors in the summer. During the winter you are more likely to see the bird on coasts and estuaries.

▲ The BUZZARD is often mistaken for the golden eagle (see p. 132), but it is a much smaller bird. In flight, you can usually recognize it by its shorter neck and wings. It can soar and glide for many kilometres without flapping its broad wings.

▼ BLACK GROUSE males collect together to dance in front of the females. The females, which are brown, choose their mates at these 'dances'.

► The RED GROUSE lives only in the British Isles, where many moorlands are set aside for rearing and shooting it. The bird is a form of the WILLOW GROUSE which lives on the continent and has white wings. In winter the willow grouse turns almost completely white. Both birds feed mainly on heather shoots.

willow grouse

red grouse

THE MEDITERRANEAN REGION

The area surrounding the Mediterranean Sea is very hot and sunny in the summer. Some places get virtually no rain from April to October. Insects revel in the heat and there are far more kinds here than in the cooler parts of Europe. Native plants have become well adapted to the climate. The trees and shrubs have tough, evergreen leaves that do not shrivel in the heat. Many of the smaller plants grow in the winter and spring, when it is often wet but still not very cold. These plants then die down and spend the summer resting under the ground. The best time to see the Mediterranean flowers is clearly in the spring.

UMBRELLA PINES *

It's not difficult to see why these trees are called umbrella pines. They grow around the coast and people often plant them in towns and gardens to provide shade. They are also called stone pines because they have very hard seeds in their cones. The seeds are good to eat when their hard coats have been removed.

139

The spongy outer bark of the trunk of the cork oak tree is used to make cork objects of all kinds. Removing the bark is a skilled job, because the tree will die if too much bark is taken away. New bark soon starts to grow and it can be cut again after about ten years, when it is between five and ten centimetres thick. A tree can give up to 20 crops of good quality cork in its lifetime.

Forests of cork oaks once grew around the Mediterranean, but you will find only scattered trees in most places now. Trees which have been stripped are easily recognized by the smooth bark on the lower part of the trunk. Most cork is now grown in Spain and Portugal.

◀ Tough, evergreen leaves withstand the hot summer sun. The acorns are just like those of other oaks.

▲ The thick, corky bark protects the trees against fire, which is very common in the Mediterranean area.

The AGAVE is a Mexican plant that was introduced to the Mediterranean region as a garden plant. It has now spread to many cliffs and rocky slopes. Mature plants send up huge sprays of flowers. The plants die as soon as they have flowered. You will see lots of dead ones by the roadside.

The crumpled appearance of CISTUS flowers is quite normal. Cistus bushes grow on rough ground all over the Mediterranean region. You will often find them under the cork oaks and the umbrella pines. Their tough, leathery leaves are often strongly scented and very sticky.

If you look under the cistus bushes in late spring you will probably find the curious CYTINUS. This is a parasitic plant, stealing all its food from the cistus roots. It never has any leaves. Some cytinus plants have pink and white flowers.

▶ The DRAGON ARUM is a giant relative of the lords-and-ladies of the hedgerow (see p. 77). You'll know when you get close to one, because it gives out a really awful smell. This is to attract small flies, which then pollinate the flowers.

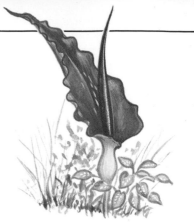

◀ The TONGUE ORCHID gets its name from the shape of the lower lip of the flower. Huge numbers grow by the roadsides in the spring, especially where the ground is damp.

▶ HOLLOW-STEMMED ASPHODEL grows on roadsides and wasteland and is also a weed in cultivated fields. It has narrow rush-like leaves and pink or white flowers.

▼ The SQUIRTING CUCUMBER is not a real cucumber, although it belongs to the same family. It gets its name because the ripe egg-shaped fruits explode and squirt out their seeds. The plant is poisonous, but it provides us with several useful medicines.

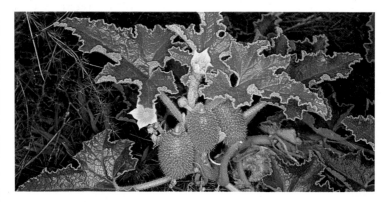

▲ The CALTROPS plant sprawls over the roadsides and waste ground and its spiny fruits often puncture bicycle tyres. It got its name from the spiked lumps of metal, called caltrops, that armies used to scatter on the ground in olden days to halt their enemies' horses. It is also called punctureweed and Maltese cross.

▼ MALLOW-LEAVED BINDWEED scrambles over rocky slopes, including many roadsides, and covers them with carpets of beautiful pink flowers.

▼ The JUDAS TREE is a native of dry, rocky slopes, where it usually bursts into flower before its leaves open. The brilliant rose-pink flowers spring straight from the older branches and the trunk. The tree is planted for ornament in many places. According to legend, this is the tree on which Judas hanged himself.

The GIANT PEACOCK MOTH, shown here at life size, is Europe's biggest insect. It is often mistaken for a bat when it is flying at dusk. Its caterpillar feeds on various trees and shrubs.

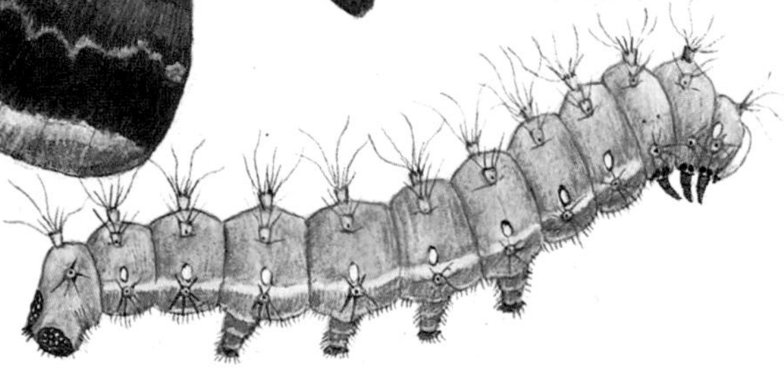

The OAK HAWKMOTH is almost entirely confined to the remaining patches of cork oak forest, where its caterpillar feeds on the oak leaves.

▲ The TWO-TAILED PASHA gets its name from the two short tails on the hind wing. It is a fast-flying butterfly that is particularly fond of ripe peaches and other fruit. It feeds on fruit much more often than it does on flowers. Its caterpillar feeds on the strawberry tree and is beautifully camouflaged amongst the leaves.

◄ The SPANISH FESTOON butterfly is one of the earliest to fly in the spring. It lives in Spain, Portugal, and southern France.

▼ The SOUTHERN FESTOON, which lives further east, has only one red spot on the front wing or none at all.

southern festoon caterpillar

The Mediterranean air is full of the sounds of insects in the summer. All day and all night they chirp and sing. It is as if the countryside were full of little sewing machines, knife-grinders, and other busy machinery.

▼ The TIZI is a plump bush cricket with tiny wings – just enough to rub together to make its song. It is called a tizi because that is just what its song sounds like. It is repeated again and again all day and all night. Both male and female can sing.

► The male CICADA sits in trees and bushes by day and gives out a shrill whistle which can be quite deafening. The sound is produced by the vibration of a tiny drum skin on each side of the body.

◄ The ITALIAN CRICKET has the sweetest song. *Grii-grii-grii* it goes, all through the evening and well into the night. But it is hard to find this insect because it is a sort of ventriloquist. It throws its voice so that you think it is moving about, but it is really sitting in the same place all the time.

▲ The GREEN LIZARD is one of the biggest and brightest of our lizards. It may be 13cm from its snout to its back legs, and then there is a very long tail. The blue throat of this one shows that it is an adult male. Green lizards often climb bushes to hunt insects. They also eat fruit and sometimes even steal eggs from birds' nests. Lizards all enjoy warmth and they are especially common in the Mediterranean area, where there are lots of different kinds. Most of them enjoy sunbathing on the rocks.

▼ The GECKO can walk up a window pane and even run upside-down on the ceiling. Its secret lies in its special toes. Each toe has a swollen tip covered with minute hairs that work like suction cups to grip the smoothest surface. The gecko hunts mainly at night. It is quite common in restaurants, where it is usually a welcome guest because it catches lots of mosquitoes and other flies.

RIVERS, LAKES AND PONDS

Most of our rivers start in the hills, where rainwater runs over the rocks and gathers to form little trickles. The trickles join up to form streams, and the streams later join forces to form the rivers. Eventually they all run into the sea. On its journey a river picks up lots of stones and carries them along. Bumping along on the bottom, the stones gradually wear away the river bed, so the river carves its way through the countryside and forms its own valley.

A huge variety of plants and animals live in and around rivers, lakes and ponds and there is always something for you to see. The waterside is one of the most fascinating of all wildlife habitats.

WATERFALLS

Waterfalls develop where rivers pass from a hard rock to a softer one. The softer rock is worn away more quickly, leaving the hard one standing up to form the lip of the fall. But even the hard rock is gradually worn away, so the falls are gradually pushed upstream.

RIVER REGIONS

The upper parts of a river look very different from the lower stretches and they have a different assortment of wildlife. In many rivers we can recognize five distinct regions or *reaches*.

The highest reach of a river is the HEADSTREAM, formed where the trickles of rainwater first join together to make a permanent channel. The water bubbles rapidly between moss-covered boulders. No fish live here, but various insect grubs feed amongst the mosses. Grey wagtails often feed on the insects.

The TROUTBECK is below the headstream. It is often formed when several headstreams join together. The water is clear and it flows rapidly over a rocky or stony bottom. The current rolls stones and boulders along the bottom, so no plants can grow there. Plenty of insect grubs hide under the stones and feed on debris brought down by the current. They are eaten by trout, which are among the few fishes strong enough to cope with the current.

lowland reach

estuary

Below the troutbeck comes the MINNOW REACH or GRAYLING REACH, named after two of its common fishes. The stream is broader and slower, with banks of gravel on which various flowering plants take root. Graceful alder trees often grow on the banks. You can recognize them by their cone-shaped catkins, which stay on the twigs all through the year. Dippers and kingfishers can be seen. Dragonflies and damselflies are common.

headstream

troutbeck

minnow reach

Still further downstream comes the LOWLAND REACH, curving gently across the flat landscape. The current is slow and the bottom is very muddy. Lots of plants grow in the water, and others grow tall on the muddy banks. This is where the fisherman and the heron can catch lots of different fishes. Roach, bream, and perch live here, together with eels and pike.

The lowest region, where the river meets the sea, is the ESTUARY. The water is salty and broad banks of mud are uncovered at low tide (see p. 171).

Lakes are large stretches of more or less still, fresh water, although most of them have streams or rivers running through them. A lake develops when a stream or a river flows into a hollow and gradually fills it up. In time, the water over-flows and cuts an escape channel, allowing the river to continue its journey to the sea.

Most of Europe's lakes, including those of England's Lake District, sit in hollows gouged out by the ice-age glaciers (see p. 10). Some of them are extremely deep.

People have created lakes in some places by damming streams and rivers, but these are usually quite small lakes. The lakes of the Norfolk Broads in England were formed when water filled up the holes made by people digging peat in the Middle Ages.

FROM POND TO DRY LAND

Ponds are smaller than lakes, although nobody can tell you just when a pond becomes a lake. Many ponds were dug to provide drinking places for farm animals, and others are just old pits that have filled up with water, but there are also plenty of ponds sitting in natural hollows. It is not always easy to say if a pond is natural or man-made. Man-made ones often have banks around them, but so do some natural ones. Most ponds contain plenty of plants, some of them completely submerged and others growing up from the shallow water around the edge.

Ponds are not permanent features. Mud is always slipping in from the banks and, together with dead plants, it builds up on the bottom. The water gets shallower and the marginal plants can spread in from the edge. They eventually meet in the middle. The pond is now a swamp, with no open water. More debris builds up around the plants and the area is gradually converted to dry land. This process is called *succession* and it can take place in lakes as well, although it would take a very long time to convert a large lake to dry land.

PLANTS OF THE POND AND RIVERSIDE

Look for these plants in ponds and in the lowland reaches of rivers. The REEDMACE, also called the bulrush, has rich brown clubs which are packed with fluffy fruits that blow away in the spring.

BROOKLIME is a kind of speedwell that grows in wet fields and marshes as well as in ponds and streams.

MONKEYFLOWER grows on rocky banks in the upper reaches of rivers as well as in the muddier parts.

ARROWHEAD has three kinds of leaves when growing in running water: strap-shaped leaves under the surface, oval floating ones, and arrow-shaped ones above the water.

WATER CROWFOOT is a white-flowered buttercup. There are several different kinds, usually with hair-like submerged leaves and broader floating ones. Some species living in fast-flowing streams have stems up to six metres long that trail out in the current.

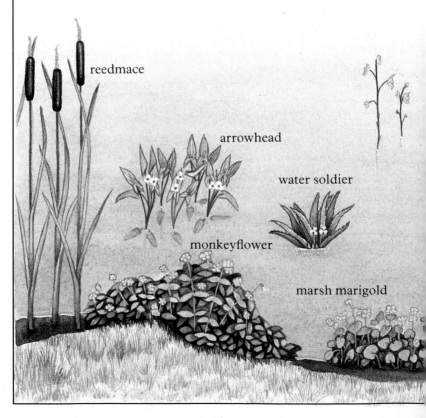

reedmace

arrowhead

water soldier

monkeyflower

marsh marigold

BLADDERWORT is an odd plant with no roots. Its thread-like leaves float in the water and catch water fleas in tiny pouches. Only if it catches enough water fleas can it send up its flowers.

MARESTAIL grows mainly in still, shallow water. Its leafy shoots sometimes form dense patches, like forests of miniature pine trees. Look for the tiny pink flowers at the bases of the leaves in the summer.

The MARSH MARIGOLD, or KINGCUP usually grows in the waterlogged ground at the edges of ponds and streams. What look like petals are really the sepals.

The POLICEMAN'S HELMET grows on river banks. It is one of several plants often called touch-me-nots, because their ripe fruits explode and throw out their seeds when they are touched. The plant gets its strange name from the shape of its flowers.

WATER SOLDIER gets its name for its stiff leaves with spiky edges that stand upright at the surface in the summer. The plants have no roots. They float in the water and sink to the bottom for the winter.

bladderwort

policeman's helmet

water crowfoot

brooklime

marestail

GRASS FOR THE ROOF

Reeds are tall grasses with tough stems. They grow in shallow water and form immense reed beds around many lakes. The stems are harvested when they are dry and woody and used for thatching houses. When bundled tightly together and fixed to a roof they will keep the water out for 60 years or more.

No two thatched roofs look exactly alike. Each part of the country has its traditional designs for thatch, and each thatcher often adds his own particular style of decoration.

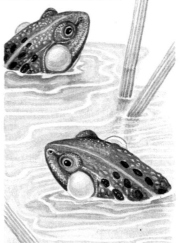

Twenty five different kinds of frogs and toads live in Europe. Frogs have smooth skins, but toad skins are usually rather bumpy.

The male MARSH FROG sounds as if it is laughing in the water. The sound is magnified by two balloon-like pouches that swell up on the throat when the frog starts to call.

*

The TREE FROG climbs trees and bushes near the water. Sticky pads on its toes help it to cling to the shiniest leaves. The male's call sound rather like a duck. Like most other frogs and toads, the tree frog spends its early life as a tadpole swimming in the water.

* midwife toad

The MIDWIFE TOAD lays her string of eggs on land and the male wraps it around his back legs. He dips the eggs in the water when they get dry, and goes right into the water when they are ready to hatch.

The otter is one of the most playful of our wild animals. Young and old animals really seem to enjoy sliding down muddy banks into the water, and they do it again and again. They also like sliding down snow-covered slopes in the winter. Otters are wonderful swimmers, twisting and diving gracefully through the water as they chase fishes to eat.

Otters are shy animals and they come out mainly at night. By day they shelter under rocks or tree roots on the river bank. These dens are called *holts*. The animals have become rare in many places because they don't like water pollution or the disturbance caused by pleasure boats. The best places to see otters are in wild areas, including some of the wilder stretches of coastline.

On the track of the otter

A good way of tracking the otter is to look for its droppings. They are black and oily when fresh and contain lots of fish bones and scales. They are often left on boulders.

FURRY FOREIGNERS

The animals on this page were all brought to Europe because they have valuable fur. They were kept on special farms, but lots of animals escaped into the countryside and now roam wild. Coypu and muskrats do a lot of damage by burrowing into river banks and causing them to collapse.

The AMERICAN MINK is a relative of the otter, but it lacks the otter's powerful tail and it can't swim nearly as well. It is only half as big as the otter. It feeds on all kinds of animals, both in and out of the water. The European mink lives mainly in eastern Europe and has more white on its face.

The COYPU is a South American rodent with a body up to 60cm long. It lives in marshy areas.

The MUSKRAT is not a rat at all – it is a large North American vole. It is smaller than the coypu and its tail is flattened from side to side.

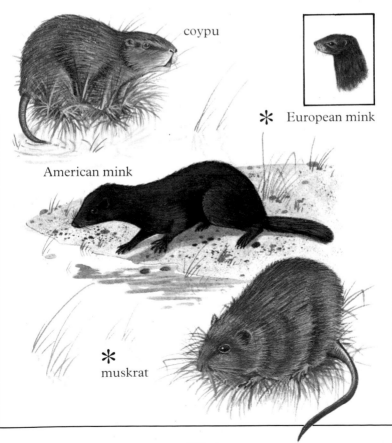

coypu

✳ European mink

American mink

✳ muskrat

▶ The LITTLE EGRET is a small *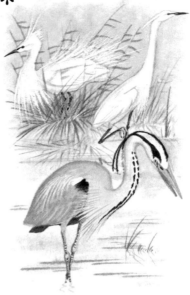
heron from southern
Europe. It picks its way
daintily through swampy
places, lifting its legs high
and showing its large
yellow feet. It eats frogs
and many other animals.

▶ The GREY HERON is a patient
fisherman, standing at the
water's edge for hours as it
waits for a fish or a frog. It
usually nests in tall trees
and there are often lots of
nests together. Like all
herons and bitterns, the
bird pulls its neck back
when it is flying.

◀ The BITTERN is more often
heard than seen. It spends
most of its time in dense
reed beds, where it is very
difficult to spot. Its deep,
booming voice sounds more
like a cow than a bird.

▶ The WHITE STORK is a *
summer visitor from Africa.
It builds huge nests in trees
and also on buildings and
telegraph poles, where
people often erect special
platforms for it. The birds
have no real voice, but
often greet each other with
loud claps of the beak.
They feed on all sorts of
waterside animals.

The MALLARD is the commonest of our wild ducks. It is the ancestor of all our farmyard ducks.

The SHOVELER gets its name for its heavy, shovel-like beak. It feeds on plants and small animals.

The TUFTED DUCK is named for the tuft of feathers on the back of its head. Don't be surprised if it suddenly disappears, for it is one of the diving ducks and it spends a lot of time looking for food under the water.

The MUTE SWAN is one of the world's heaviest birds. It can weigh over 20kg. It has no real voice, but will hiss at you if you get too near, especially if it has babies with it.

The WHOOPER SWAN and BEWICK'S SWAN both come to us from the far north for the winter. They have straighter necks than the mute swan and black and yellow beaks.

Bewick's swan

whooper swan

tufted duck

mute swan

mallard

shovelers

The GREY WAGTAIL likes fast-running streams and waterfalls. Its long tail wags all the time as it plucks insects from the ground or the water. In the winter it can be seen around lakes and farm ponds.

Male and female GREAT CRESTED GREBES dance face to face when courting, and often give each other presents of water plants. The crest and the orange neck feathers are lost for the winter.

moorhen

coot

COOTS and MOORHENS are often confused with ducks, but their beaks are not like those of the ducks, and they don't have webbed feet. Look for their footprints in the mud. Both birds like plenty of vegetation at the water's edge and they often run over the water to get back to shelter when they are frightened. The moorhen has a croaky call of *curik*, but the coot has a single syllable *kook*. Both are very loud.

THE DIPPER AND THE KINGFISHER

The DIPPER lives by fast-flowing streams in the hills. It goes under the water to catch insects and other creatures. Some dippers plunge into their streams over 1500 times a day.

The KINGFISHER stares at the water for hours. You would be dazzled by the glare if you did this for more than just a few minutes, but the kingfisher has red layers in its eyes which act like very good sunglasses. When the bird sees a fish it dives down to catch it. The bird is so quick that it can be back on its perch in about a second, with the fish in its beak.

nest burrow

kingfisher

dipper

Lots of insects live in ponds and streams. Some bugs and beetles spend all their lives there. Many other insects spend just the early part of their lives in the water.

▼ A DRAGONFLY'S eyes are nearly as big as its head. They give it the wonderful eyesight needed for catching small insects in full flight. Some dragonflies fly over the water for hours on end, but others sit on perches and fly out only when they see other insects.

Young dragonflies are called *nymphs*. They live in the water and feed on all sorts of other animals. They catch their food with a spiky jaw called a mask. It normally covers the mouth, but it is fired out at high speed to grab the food.

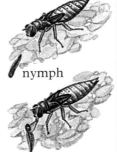

nymph

with mask extended

▼ DAMSELFLIES are small and delicate dragonflies. They can't fly very fast and they feed mainly by plucking small insects from the waterside plants.

HOUSES OF STICKS AND STONES

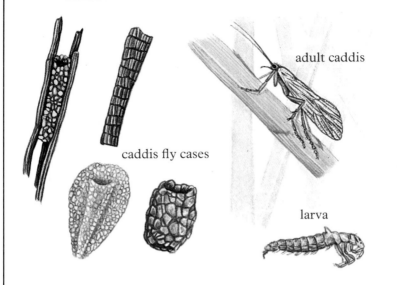

adult caddis

caddis fly cases

larva

▲ CADDIS FLIES grow up in fresh water, where most of their youngsters build themselves portable homes or cases. They use bits of twig and gravel or leaves and they fix them together with silk from their own bodies. Each kind of caddis has its own case pattern and you will probably find several different kinds by scooping up gravel and debris from the bottom of a stream and putting it in a dish of water. Look for adult caddis flies on the waterside plants. Most of them are brown or black and rather hairy. They sit with their wings held like a roof over the body and with their antennae stretched out in front.

adult mayfly

◀ MAYFLIES never go far from the water. The adults never eat and they live for no more than a few days, but they may have spent two years growing up in the water. Huge swarms of adults come out of large lakes and rivers in the summer and are often attracted to the lights of nearby towns and villages.

raft spider

raft spider

pond skater

pond skater

COMING UP FOR AIR

Animals living in the water get their oxygen direct from the water through gills, or have some way of getting air from the surface.

The RAT-TAILED MAGGOT is the grub of a hover-fly. It lives in dirty water and gets its air through a telescopic tail that it pushes up to the surface.

The WATER SPIDER has an amazing way of ensuring that it has plenty of air. It spins a thimble-shaped web among the water plants and fills it with bubbles of air brought from the surface.

Most water beetles, like the GREAT DIVING BEETLE, carry their air supplies under their tough wing cases, just as a diver carries cylinders of air. When the supply is exhausted the beetle comes up for a refill. Some come up tail-first, others head-first. You will often see them hanging from the surface while re-fuelling.

WALKING ON THE WATER

Look for POND SKATERS zooming over the surface of still or slow-moving water. If you look closely you'll see dimples where their feet rest on the surface. It's as if the water had an elastic skin on it. The pond skaters row themselves along with their long middle legs and steer with the back ones. The front legs are used to catch flies and other insects.

RAFT SPIDERS or swamp spiders also hunt on the water surface. They sit on floating leaves with their front legs resting on the water. They pick up vibrations from passing insects and dart out to catch them. These big spiders can also catch small fishes.

whirligig beetle

rat-tailed maggot

water spider

great diving beetle

HALF IN AND HALF OUT

WHIRLIGIG BEETLES zoom round on the surface like tiny speed boats. Each eye has two halves, one to look across the surface and one to look down into the water.

SOME FRESHWATER FISHES

The ROACH is one of Europe's commonest fishes. It can survive better than most fishes in polluted water.

The TENCH is a slimy fish living at the bottom of muddy ponds, lakes, canals and slow-moving rivers. It buries itself in the mud in the winter. It can survive for quite a long time out of the water.

The female BITTERLING protects her eggs by laying them inside the shell of a freshwater mussel, using a long tube on her body.

The WELS is Europe's largest freshwater fish. It may be four metres long and weigh 200kg. It eats fishes, frogs and even ducklings.

pike

tench

bitterling

miller's thumb

The MILLER'S THUMB is a spiny fish living in stony streams. It gets its odd name because its shape was thought to resemble the outline of a miller's thumb – broad and flat at the tip from years of pressing flour through sieves.

The PIKE is a ferocious fish. It is up to about 1.5 m long and it lurks in the weeds in lakes and slow-moving rivers. It darts out at high speed to catch fishes, water voles and ducklings.

The PERCH is easily recognized by its dark stripes and its red tail and lower fins. It lives mainly in weedy ponds and rivers.

The STICKLEBACK is named for the spines on its back. In the spring the male's throat turns red and he builds a nest with bits of water plants. By dancing in front of a female and showing off his red throat, he persuades her to lay her eggs in his nest. He then looks after the eggs and babies by himself.

roach

perch

stickleback

wels ✳

The SALMON and the EEL both travel a long way to lay their eggs, but they go in different directions. The salmon travels up-river from the sea and can leap up waterfalls to get to its breeding grounds in the minnow reach.

Eels go from the river to the sea and swim as much as 7,000 kilometres to the Sargasso Sea in the Atlantic Ocean. The babies take three years to get back to the European rivers. Eels can wriggle overland on wet nights.

THE FISH WITH NO JAWS

The LAMPREY is a bit like an eel at first sight, but you can easily recognize it by the seven round gill-openings on each side. The oddest thing about it is that it has no jaws. It has just a circular mouth surrounded by horny teeth. It fixes its mouth to other fishes, tears their flesh with its teeth, and then sucks their blood. It lives partly in the sea and partly in fresh water.

The estuary is the final part of the river, where the fresh water flowing down mixes with salt water brought in by the tide. At high tide the river is wide, but at low tide you see a much narrower river flowing between wide banks of mud. These mud flats are important feeding grounds for wading birds, especially in the winter. The higher parts of the banks, flooded only by the highest tides, are called *saltmarshes*. They are riddled with winding channels that carry the water away and are often covered with sea lavender flowers in the summer.

* These flamingoes live in the Camargue – the estuary of the river Rhône – in southern France. They strain tiny animals from the muddy water with their strange beaks.

171

THE COAST

The coastline is always changing, with the land being worn away in some places and built up in others. Waves gradually wear away the cliffs by crashing into them and hurling stones and boulders at them with great force.

The rocks that fall from the cliffs continue to be battered and rolled about by the waves and they are gradually worn down to rounded stones and eventually to sand. Some of the sand is washed far out to sea, but most of the material is simply moved along the coast. Waves bring it in to the shore and dump it to form beaches. The type of beach depends on the material available and also on the shape of the coast and the strength of the waves. Some beaches build up quite quickly and extend the land, but they are not necessarily permanent. Strong storms can wash away whole beaches in a few hours.

WAVE EROSION

Waves attacking both sides of a narrow headland often cut right through it to form a natural arch. Eventually the top of the arch will fall, leaving the outer part standing up as a stack. The Needles on the coast of the Isle of Wight are all stacks.

The beach is covered and uncovered by the tide twice every day. When uncovered it may be lashed by the rain, dried by the sun, or even frozen by the frost. Add to this the pounding that it receives from the waves and it is quite surprising that any plants and animals manage to survive there.

◀ Rocky beaches provide plenty of anchorages for seaweeds and plenty of nooks and crannies for animals to hide in when the tide goes out. These are the best beaches for the naturalist to explore.

▼ Sandy beaches are rather dull when the tide goes out, although there are plenty of animals hiding under the sand and waiting for the tide to return.

▶ Shingle and boulder beaches don't have much wildlife. The moving stones would squash most things, but sand hoppers survive here, feeding on plant debris. A few plants grow in the more stable shingle.

TIDES AND STRANDLINES

Twice every day the tide sweeps over the shore and drops a line of debris at its highest point. This line is called the strand line and it is well worth examining when the tide goes out again. You can find lots of seashells and other interesting things among the bits of plastic and seaweed. Lots of shrimp-like sandhoppers feed on the debris.

cuttlebone – the internal shell of a cuttlefish

empty whelk egg case

sea-ball, made of the fibres of sea grasses that have been rolled around by the waves.

mermaid's purse – the egg case of a dogfish

sandhopper

THE MOON'S INFLUENCE

You might be surprised to learn that the tides are caused by the sun and the moon. The height of the tide depends upon the position of the moon. Twice every month, at new moon and full moon, we get very high tides which come a long way up the beach. Because the tides don't all reach the same point on the beach you will often find several strand lines. The lowest one is always the newest one.

Rock pools are wonderful places for watching seashore life. Pink seaweeds often encrust the rocks and other seaweeds wave about in the water. Winkles and other snails browse on the seaweeds, while crabs and prawns scuttle about on the bottom. Fishes lurk amongst the weeds.

Colourful SEA ANEMONES look like plants but are animals. They eat fishes and anything else that bumps into their waving tentacles. Sticky threads fired by the tentacles snare the victims and poisonous darts are fired into them. Tie a small piece of meat to a thread and dangle it among an anemone's tentacles. Try to pull away and you will see just how firmly it is held.

HERMIT CRABS often live in rock pools. They have soft bodies and they live in old sea shells for protection.

SEA URCHINS often camouflage themselves with bits of shell and seaweed.

snakelocks anemone

blenny

topshell

flat periwinkle

sea urchin

hermit crab

Seaweeds grow mainly on rocky and stony shores, from around high water mark to depths of about 100 metres. They can't go much lower because it gets too dark for them to make their food.

◀ BLADDER WRACK or popweed gets its name from the air-filled bladders that buoy it up in the water.

▶ CHANNELLED WRACK can survive out of water for several days, thanks to the moisture trapped in channels along its branches.

◀ SEA LETTUCE is particularly common where streams of fresh water run into the sea.

▶ CORALWEED is a bushy seaweed coated with lime. It turns white when it dies.

▼ THONGWEED is one of the easiest seaweeds to identify.

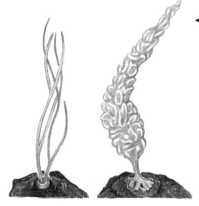

◀ SEA BELT or sugar kelp is one of Europe's biggest seaweeds, up to nine metres long. It forms thick 'forests' just below low-tide level and old fronds are often washed up on the shore. Some people use them for weather forecasting: they become dry and brittle in dry weather but become limp when rain approaches.

Sea shells are of two main kinds – the *snail shell*, which is in one piece and usually coiled, and the *bivalve*. The latter is in two halves, although the halves have usually come apart by the time the shell is washed up on the beach. See how many kinds you can find. Look for living ones on rocky shores.

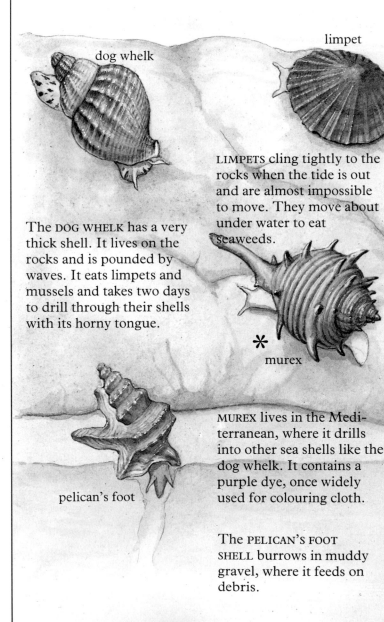

dog whelk

limpet

LIMPETS cling tightly to the rocks when the tide is out and are almost impossible to move. They move about under water to eat seaweeds.

The DOG WHELK has a very thick shell. It lives on the rocks and is pounded by waves. It eats limpets and mussels and takes two days to drill through their shells with its horny tongue.

*
murex

MUREX lives in the Mediterranean, where it drills into other sea shells like the dog whelk. It contains a purple dye, once widely used for colouring cloth.

pelican's foot

The PELICAN'S FOOT SHELL burrows in muddy gravel, where it feeds on debris.

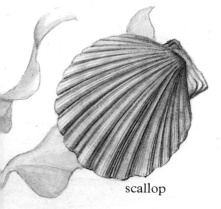

The SCALLOP is more mobile than most bivalves. It swims by flapping its valves.

scallop

The PIDDOCK uses the toothed ridges on its shell to bore its way into soft rocks and waterlogged driftwood. Once installed, it cannot escape from the burrow.

piddock

The RAZOR SHELL lives in deep, vertical burrows in the sand and can dig itself in amazingly quickly. Like all bivalves, it feeds by sucking in water and straining particles of food.

The THIN TELLIN burrows in sand and mud and uses a long tube or siphon to suck in debris from the sea bed – just like a vacuum cleaner.

thin tellin

razor shell

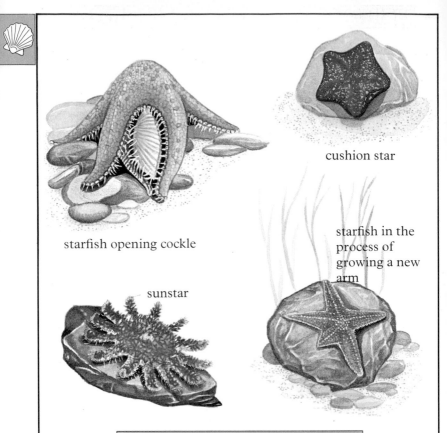

cushion star

starfish opening cockle

starfish in the process of growing a new arm

sunstar

THE POWERFUL STARFISH

Look for starfishes in rock pools or washed up on the beach. Pick one up and look at the under-side. It is covered with little suckers called *tube-feet*. The starfish uses these to pull itself along the sea bed, and also for feeding. Starfishes eat almost any kind of small animal, but they are especially fond of cockles and other bivalves. They attach their tube-feet to both halves of the shell, and the combined pull of all the suckers is enough to overcome the bivalve's own muscle power and open the shell. The starfish can then get at the soft body.

Starfishes are pests in oyster beds. The oyster farmers used to tear them in half and throw them back into the water, but they wouldn't have done if they had known about the starfish's amazing powers of recovery. Each half can grow into a complete new animal! Even a torn-off arm will often grow into a new starfish.

► Look out for the LESSER
WEEVER. It has poisonous
spines on its back and it has
the unpleasant habit of
sitting in the sand with just
the spines showing. It is
wise to wear some kind of
footwear when paddling in
areas where this fish occurs.

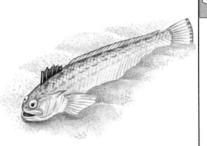

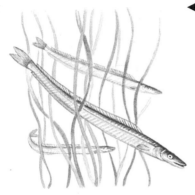

◄ SAND-EELS often burrow
into the sand when the tide
goes out. They are the
favourite food of the puffin.
It can carry up to twenty in
its beak at one time.

► The SEA-HORSE is one of
the oddest fishes in the sea.
It swims in an upright
position by whirring the
little fin on its back like a
propeller. The female lays
her eggs in a pouch on the
male's belly, and the male
actually gives birth to the
babies when they have
hatched. PIPE-FISHES are
similar but have straight
bodies.

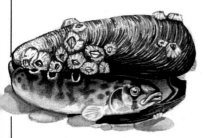

◄ The BUTTERFISH often lives
in rock pools, where it
commonly lays its eggs in
empty sea shells.

Salt is bad for most flowering plants and hardly any grow in the sea. But you can find some colourful flowers on the cliffs and on the sand and shingle above high tide level.

◀ THRIFT or sea pink forms moss-like cushions on cliffs and also in saltmarshes (see p. 171).

▼ The OYSTER PLANT grows on the shingle, mainly in northern regions. Its leaves taste like oysters. Its flowers are pink at first and then turn blue.

▼ SEA PEA creeps over shingle beaches. Its flowers are purplish red at first and then they turn blue.

▼ SEA-KALE has large clumps of cabbage-like leaves.

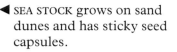

◀ SEA STOCK grows on sand dunes and has sticky seed capsules.

▶ SEA HOLLY is not related to the holly tree. It gets its name for its prickly leaves.

◀ YELLOW HORNED-POPPY gets its name for its curved seed capsules, which are up to 30cm long.

▶ GLASSWORT grows on muddy shores, especially estuaries (see p. 171). It doesn't mind being covered with sea water for long periods. It has tiny green and yellow flowers. The plant gets its name because it used to be burnt to provide a special ash used in glass making.

Lots of different kinds of sea birds live around our coasts, where they feed on fishes and other marine animals. Most of them nest on the wilder parts of the coastline in spring and early summer. At other times many of them live far out at sea.

gannet

puffins

cormorant

terns

CORMORANTS often hang their wings out to dry when they have dived to catch fishes.

The COMMON TERN is a slender-beaked cousin of the gulls. It has a forked tail and it flutters above the waves before plunging in to catch fishes.

The PUFFIN is easily recognized by its big, colourful beak. It often nests in cliff-top burrows.

The GANNET dives for fishes from a great height. Its skull is specially strengthened so that it does not hurt itself when it hits the water.

black-headed gull (summer)

fulmar

oystercatcher

black-headed gull (winter)

turnstone

The BLACK-HEADED GULL is one of the commonest gulls. Its head is actually dark brown in summer and white in the winter.

The TURNSTONE is a well-named bird. It scurries along the shore, using its slightly up-turned beak to turn over stones and seaweed searching for food.

The FULMAR is like a gull but it has tubular nostrils on top of its beak. The bird often nests on seaside buildings and it will spit smelly oil at you if you disturb it.

The OYSTERCATCHER doesn't catch oysters at all. It feeds mainly on cockles and mussels on the shore.

PEOPLE AND NATURE

A label on a cage in a New York zoo says 'You are now looking at the most dangerous animal on Earth'. The only thing in the cage is a mirror, so the only animal that the visitor sees is himself or herself. People *are* the most dangerous animals in the world. Only people can cut down forests, plough up the land, and poison the air and the water with their waste products. Of course, we must have land for our crops and houses, but there is a limit to the amount of destruction we can cause without harming the health of the whole planet. Many scientists think that we have already reached that limit.

Animals and plants have lived together for millions of years in a healthy and stable environment, but in the space of a few hundred years humans have come close to destroying it. Weather changes, including severe droughts in some places and disastrous floods in others, have been blamed on the destruction of tropical forests. Biologists think that more than 200 different kinds of plants and animals disappear from the earth *every day*, just because there is nowhere left for them to live. It is up to all of us to look after our surroundings and keep them healthy for wildlife and for ourselves. You can do your bit simply by planting a tree. Every little helps.

INDEX

The publishers wish to thank Michael Chinery for supplying photographs for this book. Other photographs supplied by:
A-Z Collection p.25.
Biofotos p. 19 (bottom three)
Peter Green, Imitor pp.14, 19 (top three).
Nature Photographers: B. Burbridge p.20; N.A. Callow p.70; P. Sterry p.94.
NHPA: B. Hawkes p.117; E.A. James p.38; E. Murtomäki p.32; Silvestris p.134; D. Woodfall p.76.
Swift Picture Library: pp.26, 40, 41 (bottom), 58, 75, 79, 151, 156 (top), 171, 174 (middle).
ZEFA: pp.6, 17, 23, 84, 95, 126, 138, 148, 152, 153, 156 (bottom), 174 (top).
Picture Research: Elaine Willis